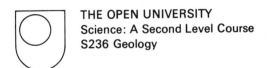

THE OPEN UNIVERSITY
Science: A Second Level Course
S236 Geology

C000044134

Block 6 Historical Geology: geological history of the British Isles

Prepared by the Course Team

Contents

The S236 Course Team

Dave Williams   (*Chairman*)
Gillian Foulkes   (*Course Coordinator*)
Joan Brown
Stuart Carter   (*BBC*)
Simon Conway Morris
Dee Edwards
Chris Hawkesworth
Peter Skelton
Richard Thorpe
David Tillotson   (*Editor*)
Sue Walker   (*Editor*)
Barrie Whatley   (*BBC*)
Chris Wilson
John Wright
Geoff Yarwood

The following people have assisted with particular parts or aspects of the Course:

Roger Beck   (*Staff Tutor*)
Norman Butcher   (*Staff Tutor*)
Janis Gilbert   (*Illustrator*)
Laurie Melton   (*Librarian*)
Pam Owen   (*Illustrator*)
Jane Sheppard   (*Designer*)
Eric Skipsey   (*Staff Tutor*)
Charles Turner

List of Blocks

Block 1   Maps
Block 2   Earth Materials
Block 3   Internal Processes
Block 4   Surface Processes
Block 5   Fossils
Block 6   Historical Geology

The Open University, Walton Hall, Milton Keynes, MK7 6AA.

First published 1983. Reprinted 1986, 1990.

Copyright © 1983 The Open University.

Designed by the Graphic Design Group of the Open University.

Typeset by Spottiswoode Ballantyne Ltd., Colchester and London and printed in Great Britain by BPCC Wheatons, Exeter.

ISBN 0 335 16140 5

This text forms part of an Open University course. For general availability of supporting material referred to in this text, please write to: Open University Educational Enterprises Limited, 12 Cofferidge Close, Stony Stratford, Milton Keynes, MK11 1BY, Great Britain.

Further information on Open University courses may be obtained from the Admissions Office, The Open University, P.O. Box 48, Walton Hall, Milton Keynes, MK7 6AB.

Table A   List of scientific terms and concepts used in this Block

Introduced in the Science Foundation Course or earlier in this Course	S101/S102* Unit No.		S236 Block No.	Introduced in the Science Foundation Course or earlier in this Course	S101/S102* Unit No.		S236 Block No.
accretionary prism			4	esker			4
aeolian			4	eustatic change (of sea-level)		28–29	1
alluvial fan			4	evaporites	27	27	
ammonite (ammonoid)		28–29		exhumed topography			1
andesite	27	7–8, 27		facies			1
angular discordance			1	fault	27	5–6, 27	1
anticline			1	fault scarp			1
arkose		SS Notes	2	ferromagnesian minerals		27	2
asymmetry (of folds)			1	fluvial (sediments)			4
axial plane (of folds)			1	folds		5–6, 27	1
basalt	4	5–6, 27		fractional crystallization	27	27	
basaltic volcanoes		27	3	gabbros	4 (AC90)	5–6	2
basement			3	genus (pl. genera)	20	21	
basin			1	geothermal gradient			3
biostratigraphic column	26	28–29		glaciation	28	28–29	
bioturbation			4, 5	glacier ice			4
boulder clay	TV06	28–29		glacifluvial deposits			4
brachiopod			5	gneiss		27	2
braided river		28–29	4	graben			1
breccia			4	granite	4 (AC90)	5–6, 27	
buried topography			1	graphic log			4
calcite	27	27		graptolites			5
cement			4	greywacke			2, 4
chert	28	28–29		gypsum			2
chronostratigraphy			5	heat flow	6/7	7–8	3
cirque			4	horst			1
cirque glacier			4	hummocky moraine			4
climatic belts (evidence for continental drift)	6/7	7–8		hydrous minerals (hydrated minerals)			2
composite volcano		27	3	ice ages	28	28–29	
cone sheets			3	ice cap		28–29	4
conformable sequence			1	igneous (rocks)	4 (AC90)	5–6	
conglomerates		SS Notes	4	inlier			1
continental drift	6/7	7–8		intrusive rocks	4 (AC90)	5–6	
continental shelf	6/7	7–8		isoclinal folds			3
continental slope	6/7	7–8		isostatic movements (isostasy)	6/7	7–8	
corals			5	island arc	6/7	7–8	3
craton	6/7 (AC90)	7–8		kame			4
crinoid		28–29	5	kettle hole			4
cross-bedding		27	4	limestone	4 (AC90)	5–6	
crustal shortening			3	listric fault			3
daughter isotope	26	28–29		lithology			1
deep-sea drilling samples	6/7	7–8		lithostratigraphy			5
delta			4	magma	4	5–6	
desert			4	mantle (upper, lower)	4	5–6	
destuctive plate margins	6/7	7–8		mass movement			4
dextral (fault)			1	marine transgression			4
diapir	27	27	3	matrix			4
dip			1	matrix support			4
dome			1	meander			4
downthrow			1	micrite			4
drift			1	microfossil		27	5
drumlin			4	molluscs			5
dune		SS Notes	4	nappe			3
dyke	26	7–8		normal fault		27	1
erratic			4				

Introduced in the Science Foundation Course or earlier in this Course	S101/S102* Unit No.		S236 Block No.	Introduced in the Science Foundation Course or earlier in this Course	S101/S102* Unit No.		S236 Block No.
ocean crust	4	5–6		sea-floor spreading	6/7	7–8	
ocean ridge	6/7	7–8		sedimentary rocks	4	5–6	
ocean trench	6/7	7–8		seismic	4	5–6	
ooids			2	shield volcanoes		7–8	3
ooze	27	27		siliciclastic (sediments)			4
orogenesis			3	sills		28–29	3
outcrop		28–29	1	slates		27	2
paired metamorphic belt			3	sorting		27	4
palaeocurrent directions			4	strata		28–29	1
parent isotope	26	28–29		stratigraphic	26	28–29	1
peridotite	4	5–6		strike			1
periglacial (conditions, climate)			1, 4	stromatolites	28	28–29	
Period (of geological time)	26	28–29		subduction	6/7	7–8	
permafrost			4	submarine fan			4
Phanerozoic			1	suspension deposits			4
pillow lavas		5–6	3	symmetry (of folds)			1
planar bedding			4	syncline			1
planktonic		25	5	tear faulting			1
plate tectonics	6/7	7–8		thrust	27	27	
playa lake			4	thrust fault		27	1
pluton			3	till		7–8	4
polar wandering curves	6/7	5–6		tillite			4
progradation			4	trace fossils			5
province (faunal)			5	traction deposits			4
pyroclastic rocks		27	3	transcurrent fault			1, 3
radial dykes			3	trilobites		28–29	5
radioactive (elements)	10/11	11–12		tuff			3
regression, marine			4	turbidite			4
relief			1	turbidity current			4
reverse fault		5–6	1	ultrabasic rocks			2
rhyolite		27	3	unconformity	26	28–29	1
ring dykes		5–6	3	underplating			3
rift valley			1	valley glacier			4
ripple			4	volcanic rocks		7–8	3
sandstone	4 (AC90)	5–6		wadi			4
sea-floor magnetic anomalies	6/7	7–8		Walther's law			4

* The Open University (1979) S101 *Science: A Foundation Course*, The Open University.
  The Open University (1988) S102 *A Science Foundation Course*, The Open University.

Introduced or developed in this Block	Page No.	Introduced or developed in this Block	Page No.	Introduced or developed in this Block	Page No.
accretionary prism model for the Southern Uplands	28	Carboniferous palaeogeography	42	Late Cretaceous sea-level high	50
'Alpine' folding and faulting	54	Carboniferous cyclothem	41	Loch Lomond readvance	67
Basement (Precambrian)	13, 20	cover unit	10	litho-tectonic unit	10
basins and swells	54	Devonian palaeogeography	38	metamorphic Caledonides	13
Caledonian Orogenic Belt	7, 13, 22	emergent area	32	Mid-Cretaceous faulting	54
Caledonian post-orogenic granites	34	epeirogenic sea-level change	7	Midland Valley (of Scotland)	12
Caledonian plate tectonic model	34	eustatic sea-level change	7	Moine Thrust Zone	13
Caledonian structural trend	13	glacial–interglacial cycles	64	New Red Sandstone fault-bounded basins	53
Carboniferous blocks and basins	40	Gondwanaland	42	Newer Drift	67
		Highland Boundary Fault	12	non-metamorphic Caledonides	13
		Iapetus Ocean	22		
		Iapetus suture	33		

Introduced or developed in this Block	Page No.	Introduced or developed in this Block	Page No.	Introduced or developed in this Block	Page No.
Old Red Sandstone	35	Permo-Carboniferous		Tertiary igneous activity	51
Older Cover	11, 34, 37	igneous activity	51	Variscan Orogenic Belt	7, 12, 34, 44
Older Drift	67	Precambrian Basement	13, 20	Wales–London–Brabant	
orogenic unit	10	Rheic Ocean	45	Massif	40
Pangaea	7	rift-to-sag pattern	16	Yoredales	41
Permian deserts	56	Southern Uplands Fault	12	Younger Cover	10, 48
Permian evaporites	57	St George's Land	36	Zechstein Sea	57

Study guide

The purpose of this Block is to provide you with a brief geological history of the British Isles. The story that unfolds in the text is based on your knowledge of geological principles gained during this Course, and on the evidence *you* should be able to interpret from the outcrop patterns on the Ten Mile Maps. Therefore, you should pay particular attention to the list in Table A of pre-requisite knowledge assumed from previous Blocks in the Course; this provides a useful guide to pre-examination revision! You will notice that there are relatively few totally *new* terms introduced in this Block, and many of those that are new concern the geological features of specific areas or geological Periods. In addition to the Ten Mile Maps, you will also need the Cheddar Sheet, the Lake District Map, the Moreton-in-Marsh Map, and the Colour-plate Booklet for Blocks 5 and 6.

As a common approach is used in Sections 3 and 5–8 of this Block, no study comments additional to these are included. Each of these Sections begins with a variety of ITQ exercises involving the interpretation of aspects of the Ten Mile Maps, and then continues with a more detailed discussion of a particular episode in the geological history of the British Isles. If you are short of time, you could skip some of these ITQs, but make sure you read the answers to them, as these are crucial to an understanding of many of the concepts discussed in this Block.

Unlike many historical geology texts used in conventional introductory geology courses, this Block does not attempt to give a concise summary of as many aspects as possible of British geological history. Instead, the main aim is to paint a broad historical picture of the tectonic, climatic and palaeogeographic evolution of the British Isles based very much on evidence from the Ten Mile Maps. Guidance on the amount of factual information you should be able to recall is provided through the Table A terms. Items indicated in this way are key features in the geological history of the British Isles, and are regarded as the kind of basic knowledge you should possess after finishing this Course.

This Block is 1½ Course Unit equivalents in study time, very roughly dividing into: Sections 1–4, ½ CUE; Sections 5–7, ½ CUE; and Sections 8 and 9, ½ CUE. TV 16 is a revision programme, both for this Block and the whole Course.

1 Introduction

Look at Colour Plates 6.1–6.6 (in the Colour-plate Booklet for Blocks 5 and 6), which are artists' impressions of what parts of the British Isles looked like during different periods of the region's geological history. You can see that the British Isles experienced a range of climates during the past four or five hundred million years, from deserts and equatorial forests to the cold of the ice ages. Not only did the climate change, but so did sea-levels and *relief*^{A} on land, and at times, parts of the British Isles experienced volcanic activity.

The purpose of this Block is to take you on a geological tour of the British Isles to explore how these changes can be discerned in the rock record. But it will not be a simple 'Cook's tour', for on occasions *you* will be asked to interpret data, using the knowledge and skills you have gained while studying the earlier parts of this Course. After all, Blocks 3, 4 and 5 were concerned with the methods by which past environments—within the crust, and on it in the oceans and atmosphere—can be interpreted from observations concerning rocks.

2 A global view of Earth history

In contrast to the treatment of Earth history in the Science Foundation Course* (which dealt mainly with the origins of the Solar System, the Earth and its oceans and atmosphere, and with the origin of life), this Block takes a relatively narrow view, concentrating on the last 700 million years history of a tiny part of the globe. But it is important not to lose track of the fact that events in the geological history of Britain are often local reflections of world-wide events.

> Can you recall from the Science Foundation Course the underlying cause of the climatic changes in Britain over the past 700 Ma, some of which are illustrated by Colour Plates 6.2–6.6?

As the British area drifted northwards, it crossed different *climatic belts*^{A} starting somewhere near the south pole 620 Ma ago and crossing the equator some 290 Ma ago (Colour Plate 6.4). The palaeoclimatic evidence for *continental drift*^{A} is supported by *polar wandering curves*^{A} as shown in Figure 1. These curves not only confirm the northward drift of the British area as indicated by palaeoclimatic evidence, but also show that the present-day Atlantic Ocean began to open about 200 Ma ago.

> Why do the curves from 550 Ma to 390 Ma converge on Figure 1(b)?

This convergence indicates that the North American and British regions were separated from one another at 550 Ma, but had come together by 390 Ma.

> Can you recall what happens when previously separated continents collide?

Ocean crust^A separating them is 'consumed' by *subduction*^{A} until continental collision occurs producing an *orogenic*^{A} belt. Former orogenic belts contain a variety of features (which will be discussed in Section 3), such as *volcanic rocks*^{A}, *granitic*^{A} *intrusions*^{A}, *sedimentary rock*^{A} successions, intense deformation (*folds*^{A} and *thrust faults*^{A}), and metamorphic rocks, which enable the nature and timing of past ocean closing and continental collision episodes to be interpreted. The geology of the British area is dominated by two orogenic belts, the Caledonian and Variscan belts, which are continuous on either side of the Atlantic (see Figure 2). Later Sections of this Block will discuss the distribution and nature of these orogenic belts in the British Isles.

---

* S101, Unit 28 *Earth History*.

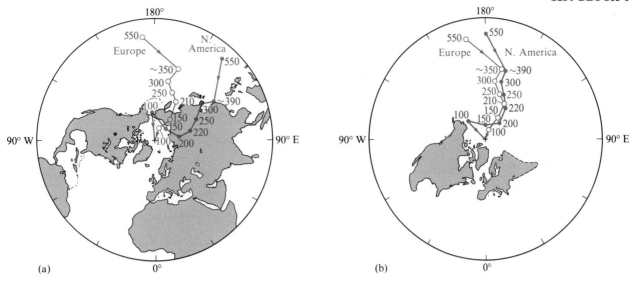

Figure 1 Apparent polar wandering curves for Europe and North America. (a) with the continents in their present day positions; (b) with the Atlantic closed by rotating the continents back together. The divergence of the two curves beyond 390 Ma may be explained by the former presence of an ocean (a 'proto-Atlantic', often called the Iapetus Ocean) separating the two continents.

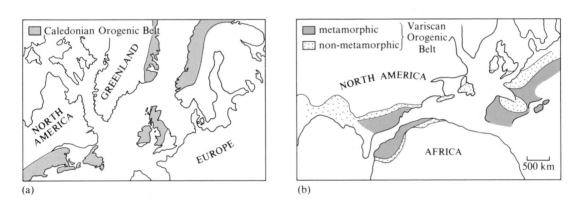

Figure 2 The distribution of (a) the Caledonian and (b) Variscan Orogenic Belts on either side of the present-day North Atlantic Ocean. These belts were produced by separate ocean closing/continental collision episodes. The present day fragmentation of these belts on either side of the Atlantic is strong evidence in favour of the hypothesis that continents now bordering the Ocean were once united.

Careful examination of Figure 3 will show that during the past 500 Ma, the British area has been part of large continental masses, and even split between different continents (see Figure 3a). The *Caledonian Orogenic Belt* contains rocks formed within, and on the flanks of, an ocean that once separated Scotland from the rest of present-day Britain (Figure 3a). By 380 Ma ago (Figure 3b), this ocean had closed, with the resultant continental collision producing major tectonic structures that are discernible on the Ten Mile Map. Likewise, the *Variscan Orogenic Belt* was the culmination of a later period of ocean closure and continental collision, which led to the unification of all the main masses of continental crust into one super-continent termed *Pangaea* (Figure 3d). Figures 3(e) and 3(f) show stages in the break-up of Pangaea, which resulted in not only the formation of new oceans, but yet another orogenic belt, as Africa collided with Europe to produce the Alps, and India with Asia to form the Himalayas. These last two examples illustrate that orogenic episodes may occur at the same time as ocean opening. This is hardly surprising, as the theory of *plate tectonics*[A] envisages subduction, lateral continental movement and collision to be the result of *sea-floor spreading*[A].

A detailed discussion of the causes of relative sea-level changes is beyond the scope of this Course. Such changes may affect the whole globe at once, in which case they are termed *eustatic changes*[A], or may be more local and due to orogenic or *isostatic*[A] earth movements. The latter are termed *epeirogenic sea-level changes*. Eustatic sea-

Caledonian Orogenic Belt

Variscan Orogenic Belt

Pangaea

eustatic sea-level change
epeirogenic sea-level change

7

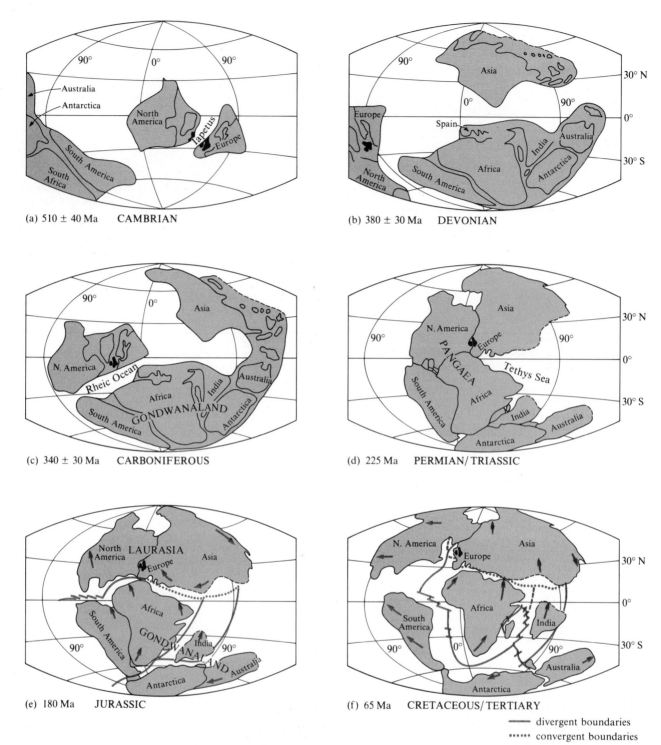

(a) 510 ± 40 Ma   CAMBRIAN

(b) 380 ± 30 Ma   DEVONIAN

(c) 340 ± 30 Ma   CARBONIFEROUS

(d) 225 Ma   PERMIAN/TRIASSIC

(e) 180 Ma   JURASSIC

(f) 65 Ma   CRETACEOUS/TERTIARY

——— divergent boundaries
•••••• convergent boundaries

Figure 3 Reconstructions of past continental configurations. Note how the British Isles (*black*) were once split between two separate continents/tectonic plates (a), and the considerable dextral movement between North America and Gondwanaland from (b) and (c).

level changes have been charted through *Phanerozoic*[A] time; the resultant curve is shown in Figure 4.

Compare the curve shown in Figure 4 with the maps in Figure 3 showing the changing assembly of continental masses through time. Can you detect any correlation between sea-level and the degree of unification of the continental masses?

There does seem to be a crude correlation; the sea-level low between 300 and 200 Ma ago corresponds to the time when all the continents were united into Pangaea (Figure 3d). Sea-level highs before and after this period correspond to times when the continents were drifting apart.

What might be the reason for this correlation?

Consider how *global* changes of sea-level might be caused. The link between *glaciation*[A] and eustatic sea-level changes is that the formation of thick *ice caps*[A]

8

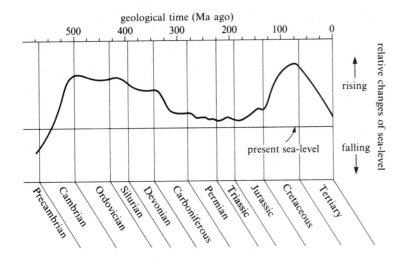

Figure 4 Relative changes in global sea-levels during the Phanerozoic. Note that the present sea-level shown is the average for the Pleistocene, a period affected by major glaciations. This is why the sea-level curve does not meet the present sea-level line.

reduces the volume of water in the oceans causing a eustatic fall. Melting of the ice causes a sea-level rise.

Table 1 summarizes the occurrence of major *ice ages*[A] over the past 700 Ma. How well do these data correlate with the Phanerozoic global sea-level curve shown in Figure 4?

Table 1 The occurrence of ice ages in the geological record

Ice age	Approximate age	Geological Period	Areas yielding evidence
Quaternary	0–4 Ma	Pliocene–Pleistocene	Many
Permo-Carboniferous	270–310 Ma	Carboniferous–Permian	Brazil, North Africa
Late Ordovician	450 Ma	Ordovician–Silurian	Southern Hemisphere
	600–650 Ma		Scandinavia, Scotland, Greenland, China, Africa
	750 Ma	Precambrian	Australia, China, South-west Africa
	900 Ma		Greenland, Scandinavia, Spitsbergen
	c. 2 300 Ma		Canada, USA, South Africa

There is a good correlation between the sea-level 'lows' and the Quaternary and Carboniferous–Permian glaciations, but global sea-levels were *high* during the late Ordovician glaciation. So glaciation alone cannot account for the observed sea-level changes. In fact it is now believed that such global changes are caused by glaciations *and* another cause. This second cause *can* be related to the changing continental configurations illustrated in Figure 3. As a super-continent, such as Pangaea (Figure 3d) breaks up, a new system of *ocean ridges*[A] forms and displaces water in the oceans, so causing continental flooding. Thus this process, instead of changing the *volume of water* in the oceans (as with glaciation), changes the *volume of the oceanic container*, so that seawater may either spill onto the continents or retreat to their edges. The sea-level highs that peaked during the Early Palaeozoic and Cretaceous are therefore probably due to an increase in ocean spreading activity.

The Cretaceous 'high' was probably some 300 m (1 000 ft!) above present-day sea-level, and not surprisingly, as you will see later, its effect can be detected on the Ten Mile Map.

You should now be able to see how the three themes of plate tectonics, climatic change and sea-level change are interlinked. These themes will recur throughout this Block as we examine the geology of the British Isles.

3 The main groups of rocks in Britain

3.1 Introduction

In the previous Section, we saw that the Phanerozoic history of the British Isles was punctuated by two major periods of earth movement referred to as the Caledonian and Variscan orogenies. Both these episodes involved the collision of continental plates, with the result that the crust was considerably thickened, thus inducing isostatic uplift. The resultant mountain chain was then rapidly eroded, and eventually worn almost flat, so that at times of sea-level rise the area was overwhelmed by the sea. The result of this chain of events is a major *unconformity*ᴬ of the kind examined in the Yorkshire Pennines in Block 1. Figure 5 recapitulates the origin of such an unconformity. The geological structure of Britain can be interpreted on a large scale in terms of the events depicted on Figure 5 by recognizing *orogenic units* and *cover units* as described on the Figure. As you will see, the apparently complex *outcrop*ᴬ patterns exhibited by the Ten Mile Maps can be simplified into *five* main units—the Younger Cover, the Older Cover, the Variscan and Caledonian Orogenic Belts, and the Precambrian Basement—each of which has a distinct geological history. These units cannot be correlated exactly with *Periods*ᴬ of geological time, for they are characterized by both *lithology*ᴬ and tectonic structure. They may therefore be termed *litho-tectonic units*. The distribution of these units is shown on Figure 6. The key to this Figure is not fully explained here because in a series of ITQs you will explore its meaning, using evidence from the Ten Mile Map.

orogenic unit   cover unit

litho-tectonic units

3.2 Younger Cover

Examine the outcrop patterns on the Ten Mile Maps of the *strata*ᴬ that occupy the area shown as *Younger Cover* on Figure 6, and answer the following questions:

> **ITQ 1**   What is the *stratigraphic*ᴬ age range of the strata that make up the Younger Cover; use the terms shown in the keys to the Ten Mile Map.

> **ITQ 2**   What is the nature of its contact with the older litho-tectonic units (the Older Cover, the Orogenic Belts and the Precambrian Basement)?

It is worth exploring this unconformable relationship at a few localities in order to demonstrate that it is everywhere a large *angular discordance*ᴬ. Examine the outcrop of 85 on the Ten Mile Map (S) between Watchet on the south Bristol Channel coast (ST(31)0744) and Exeter (SX(20)99). Look at the western limit of the outcrop strip (its *base*), and decide whether it rests on rocks of the same age all along its length. In the north, it starts on 77–8 (Devonian), but going south, it rests on successively *younger* strata (78–80, 81–3 Carboniferous). South of the Exeter area, west of Torbay (SX(20)96), it can be seen resting on 77 once more. Moreover, the general *strike*ᴬ direction of 85 is north–south (ignoring the east–west tongue that extends through Crediton, filling a valley cut before deposition) in contrast to the east–west strike of the Carboniferous. So, in south-west England, there is clear evidence for an angular discordance at the base of the Younger Cover. Earlier in the Course, in Block 1, you spent some time studying the base of the Younger Cover on a larger scale map, the 1:25 000 Cheddar Sheet. Here, Triassic rather than Permian rocks form its base, but there is still an angular discordance, and the unconformity surface is very irregular, representing a *buried topography*ᴬ. Almost wherever you look on the Ten Mile Maps, you will find that whereas the age of the base of the Younger Cover is either Permian or Triassic, it always (except where faulting occurs) rests unconformably on older rocks, including in places metamorphic rocks (e.g. near Cromarty (NH(28)7967) 97–9 on 8, Moinian).

> **ITQ 3**   What is the nature of the folding affecting the Younger Cover? Describe the general trends of the *axial planes*ᴬ and *symmetry*ᴬ of the folds.

> **ITQ 4**   On Figure 6, there are contours showing the regional thickness variations of the Younger Cover. What do you notice about the contrast in its thicknesses between onshore and offshore areas?

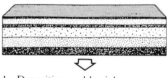

1. Deposition and burial

2. Orogeny and erosion

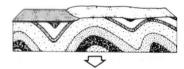

3. Transgression

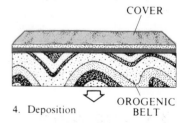

COVER

4. Deposition   OROGENIC BELT

Figure 5   The development of a major angular unconformity and the relationship between what are termed in the text *orogeny* and *cover*. Sometimes the orogenic belt beneath a cover unit is referred to as 'basement'.

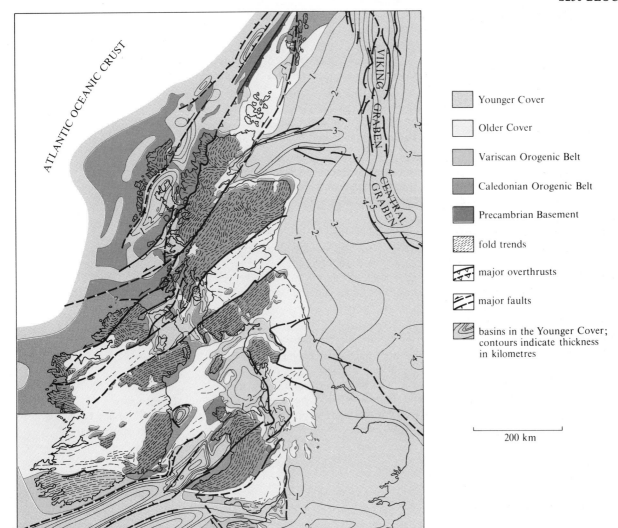

Figure 6 Sketch map of the British Isles depicting the main structural features and the distribution of the five principal litho-tectonic units. The litho-tectonic units are explored in ITQs 1–20; the meaning of the general terms orogeny and cover is explained in Figure 5.

The Younger Cover comprises a sequence of broadly *conformable*[A] strata of post-Carboniferous age, which rests with a marked angular discordance on older units, and which have been gently folded.

As you will learn in Section 8, the development of the Younger Cover was influenced largely by:

erosional and depositional processes following the uplift of the Variscan Orogenic Belt;

the global rise of sea-level during the Mesozoic (see Figure 4); and

tectonic and *igneous*[A] events associated with the opening of the Atlantic Ocean.

3.3 Older Cover

Examine the outcrop patterns on the Ten Mile Maps within the areas shown as *Older Cover* on Figure 6, and make notes answering the following questions.

Older Cover

> **ITQ 5** What is the stratigraphic age range of the Older Cover? Answer in terms of the information on the Ten Mile Maps.

ITQ 6   Where do significant amounts of volcanic rock occur in the Older Cover?

ITQ 7   Describe, in a few words only, the nature of the contact of the Older Cover with the rocks of the Caledonian Orogenic Belt (as also shown on Figure 6) in the following areas:

(a) Around the Moray Firth (north of Inverness NH(28)64) in northern Scotland; the Southern Uplands of Scotland (between the Solway Firth north of Annan NY(35)1966 and Berwick-upon-Tweed NU(46)0053); the Lake District; and north and central Wales.

(b) On the northern and southern sides of the Midland Valley of Scotland, between Helensburgh (NS(26)2982) and Stonehaven (NO(37)8786) and between Girvan (NX(25)1898) and Dunbar (NT(36)6879).

ITQ 8   (a) What is the name of the geological structure that has resulted in the preservation of a NE–SW trending area of Older Cover in the Midland Valley, sandwiched between older Caledonian Orogenic Belt rocks?

(b) Describe the nature of the folding in the Older Cover shown on the Ten Mile Map (S) in the Pennines between Manchester (SJ(33)89) and Sheffield (SK(43)38).

The Older Cover consists of a series of broadly conformable Devonian and Carboniferous strata, which rest with a marked angular discordance on the Caledonian Orogenic Belt or are faulted against it. The most significant faults, which bound the *Midland Valley* rift of Scotland, are the NE–SW trending *Highland Boundary Fault* and *Southern Uplands Fault*. Some folds are also present such as the north–south trending Pennine anticline.

Midland Valley
Highland Boundary Fault
Southern Uplands Fault

3.4   Variscan Orogenic Belt

The purpose of ITQs 9–13 is to explore the geology of the area shown as the *Variscan Orogenic Belt* on Figure 6.

Variscan Orogenic Belt

ITQ 9   What is the stratigraphic age of the rocks present within the Variscan Orogenic Belt? Answer in terms of the information given in the key to the Ten Mile Map (S).

ITQ 10   What are the major igneous intrusions present within the Variscan Orogenic Belt?

ITQ 11   Describe the nature of the folding you can infer within the Variscan Orogenic Belt from the evidence available on the Ten Mile Maps. Examine the Cheddar Sheet as well as the Ten Mile Map.

ITQ 12   On Figure 6, the boundary between the Variscan Orogenic Belt and the Older Cover is shown as a distinct line. On the basis of the nature of the folds you can infer from the outcrop evidence on the Ten Mile Map, do you think you can spot where this line runs, or do you think there is in reality a gradation from intense deformation of the orogenic belt to the gently folded Older Cover?

ITQ 13   Is it possible to detect what *underlies* the Variscan Orogenic Belt from the evidence on the Ten Mile Map?

The Variscan Orogenic Belt consists of intensely deformed strata of Late Palaeozoic age exposed in south-west England. The intensity of the folding is not apparent on the scale of outcrop patterns shown on the Ten Mile Map, which are the expression of an east–west trending syncline. In south Wales and the Mendips, the intensity of the folding is clearly greater than that examined earlier in the Younger Cover and Older Cover, but is *less* than that seen in south-west England. Thus the intensity of Variscan deformation decreases to the north, making it difficult to define precisely the boundary between the Variscan Orogenic Belt and the Older Cover. The Variscan Orogenic Belt in south-west England is intruded by a large granite body, the present-day outcrop pattern of which is caused by upward projecting protuberances from the main igneous mass. The existence of this mass at depth has been deduced from geophysical surveys.

3.5 Caledonian Orogenic Belt and Precambrian Basement

The purpose of ITQs 14–20 is to explore the geology of the area shown as the *Caledonian Orogenic Belt* on Figure 6 by examining the Ten Mile Map. Two of the ITQs refer to the (*Precambrian*) *Basement*[A]. This Basement consists of rocks that are either *older* than those of the Caledonian Orogenic Belt, or that were left *unscathed* by Caledonian events. In the case of north-west Scotland, the Basement also includes Lower Palaeozoic sediments *that were not subjected to Caledonian orogenic processes*. In this region, the Basement occupies a structurally similar position to the basement beneath the Helvetic and Pennine sediments in the Alps shown on Figure 111 of Block 3. Throughout this Block, Basement (with a capital B) implies the Precambrian Basement in the sense used in this Section, whereas basement (with a small b) is used to indicate any other rocks underlying a covering litho-tectonic unit (for example, the orogenic belt in Figure 5 could be called basement).

Caledonian Orogenic Belt
Precambrian Basement

ITQ 14   Which part of the Caledonian Orogenic Belt can be described as metamorphic, and which as non-metamorphic?

ITQ 15   What is the stratigraphic age range of rocks in the non-metamorphic part?

ITQ 16   What are the trends of the major fold structures and outcrops in the non-metamorphic part of the Caledonian Belt? Start to answer this question by examining the central and north Wales area on the Ten Mile Map, and then move on to look at the strike of outcrops or fold trends in the Lake District and Southern Uplands of Scotland.

ITQ 17   What is the relationship between the non-metamorphic Caledonides and the underlying Basement? Look at the Anglesey area, and the coastal strip south-west of Bangor (SH(23)5972) on the Ten Mile Map.

ITQ 18   Can you detect any trends in the strike of outcrops or fold trends in the metamorphic part of the Caledonian Belt?

ITQ 19   What is the relationship between the metamorphic part of the Caledonian Belt and the underlying Basement in north-west Scotland?

ITQ 20   Like the Variscan Orogenic Belt, the Caledonian Belt contains large granitic intrusions. Are these confined to certain geographic regions, or to either the metamorphic or non-metamorphic parts?

The Caledonian Orogenic Belt can be divided into two parts. To the north of the Highland Boundary Fault occur the *metamorphic Caledonides*, whereas from the Southern Uplands southwards occur the *non-metamorphic Caledonides*. The strike of the outcrop patterns and fold axial trends in both these areas follow a NE–SW *Caledonian structural trend*. Significant amounts of volcanic rocks occur in the non-metamorphic Caledonides, and can be seen on the Ten Mile Map in the Lake District, north and south Wales and the Welsh Borders. In north Wales and the Welsh Borders, the pre-Caledonian Basement lies unconformably beneath rocks of the orogenic belt, but in north-west Scotland, the boundary is tectonic and is termed the *Moine Thrust Zone*.

metamorphic Caledonides
non-metamorphic Caledonides

Caledonian structural trend

Moine Thrust Zone

3.6 Summary

You have now identified the main structural or stratigraphic units of the British Isles depicted on Figure 6. These are from top to bottom:

Younger Cover: relatively undeformed or gently folded Permian, Mesozoic and Tertiary sedimentary rocks.

Older Cover: relatively unfolded but sometimes faulted Devonian and Carboniferous sediments, with important volcanics especially in central Scotland.

The Variscan Orogenic Belt: Devonian and Carboniferous sediments generally showing east–west fold axes, and intruded by a large granite mass.

Caledonian Orogenic Belt: the dominant structural trend in these terrains is NE–SW. In the north-west Highlands, metamorphic rocks predominate and so this area is referred to as the metamorphic Caledonides. The non-metamorphic Caledonides to the south are Lower Palaeozoic sediments and contain significant volcanic sequences. Large granitic intrusions penetrate both types of Caledonian terrains, but do not occur in Wales.

Precambrian Basement: rocks that underly the other units, with either tectonic or unconformable contacts. The Basement is mostly Precambrian in age, but sediments of Cambrian and Ordovician age occur in north-west Scotland.

There is one further unit, which is not shown on Figure 6, and that is the relatively thin cover of Pleistocene *drift*[A] that mantles many outcrops of the units listed above. These sediments, and many land forms in highland areas of Britain record the glacial events of the Pleistocene that did so much to sculpture our landscape over the past few hundreds of thousands of years. These events are the subject of Section 9 of this Block.

4 Plate tectonics—a recapitulation

4.1 Introduction

In completing the ITQs in the previous Section, you described some of the features of two orogenic belts: the Caledonian and Variscan. Thus, at a very simple level, you identified the former presence of two *destructive plate margins*[A], or strictly, the final phases of ocean closure which resulted in the collision of two continents, a process that is depicted at the bottom of Figure 7. In this Section, we explore the extent to which it is possible to detect earlier phases in the cycle of ocean opening and closure; in other words, how can we identify the products of the stages shown on Figure 7? This question can be broken down into some more specific ones concerning how we might identify:

the initial rifting and separation of continents (Figure 7, top two stages);

the former presence of a wide ocean (Figure 7, 'sea-floor spreading');

the closure of an ocean by subduction (Figure 7, 'subduction');

the collision of two continents once an ocean has closed (Figure 7, bottom).

Individual features, such as andesitic lavas, basaltic lavas, granite plutons, severe folding or high grade regional metamorphism, should NEVER by themselves be taken as unequivocal evidence for the occurrence of a particular type of plate margin. It is essential to consider ALL the geological evidence, and equally important, how such evidence fits together on a regional basis. Even if such detective work is successful in helping us identify former plate boundaries, or mid-plate features, it cannot indicate how wide a once-vanished ocean might have been, even though we can often detect where the 'join' or 'suture zone' marking its closure might be located.

4.2 Continental extension, rifting and separation

A generalized model for continental rifting and separation has been developed from studies of the East African rift systems and the Red Sea (regions regarded as representing continental rifting and the earliest phases of ocean opening, respectively) and the continental margins of South Australia and the Atlantic Ocean.

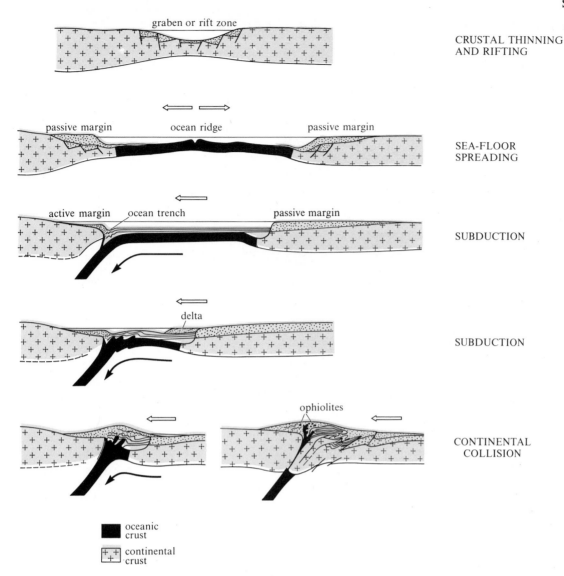

graben or rift zone

CRUSTAL THINNING
AND RIFTING

passive margin   ocean ridge   passive margin

SEA-FLOOR
SPREADING

active margin   ocean trench   passive margin

SUBDUCTION

delta

SUBDUCTION

ophiolites

CONTINENTAL
COLLISION

■ oceanic
crust

continental
crust

Figure 7 Sequence of events in the opening and closing of an ocean, culminating in continental collision. It is also possible for *both* margins of an ocean to experience subduction (see, for example, Figure 22, Section 6.5). (Ophiolites are pieces of oceanic crust that have been obducted—thrust upward—rather than subducted.)

This model is illustrated in Figure 8. This Figure shows the features that taken together can indicate past episodes of continental rifting and the development of continental margins adjacent to opening oceans. The following stages can be recognized (each is illustrated in Figure 8):

(a) *Continental rift stage*: rifting, comparable to the East African rift systems, forms a graben into which pour *fluvial*[A] *siliciclastic*[A] sediments. Lake sediments, *evaporites*[A] or even shallow marine sediments may occur if the sea is able to invade the newly created fault-bounded trough. As the water bodies, be they marine or fresh, are restricted in area, stagnation is likely, causing oxygen-deficient conditions at the bottom, which result in the preservation of organic matter. The resultant organic-rich sediments may be potential oil source-rocks. Regional uplift may result in siliciclastic sediments being shed laterally *away* from the rift zone. Volcanic rocks are associated with the rifting and uplift; they are generally basaltic lavas and *dykes*[A].

(b) '*Red Sea*' *stage*: this stage marks the development of an embryonic ocean along the site of the earlier rift. Thus the assemblage of igneous rocks characteristic of ocean crust is developed, namely sea-floor basaltic *pillow lavas*[A] underlain by basaltic dykes, beneath which occur *gabbros*[A] and *peridotites*[A] (see Block 3, Figure 33). As the embryonic ocean is narrow, water circulation is still restricted (as in the previous stage) and so organic rich and/or evaporitic sediments may accumulate. Rapid subsidence occurs as the rifted crustal blocks slide oceanwards along *listric faults*[A].

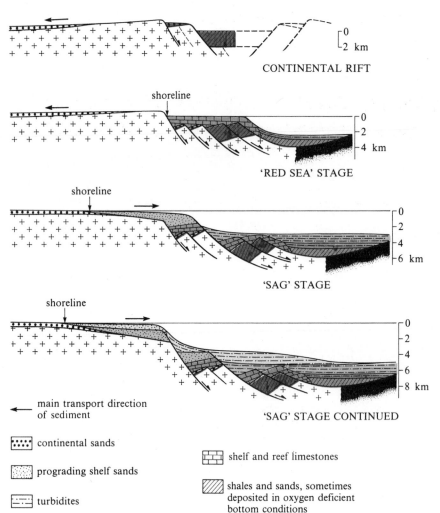

CONTINENTAL RIFT

'RED SEA' STAGE

'SAG' STAGE

'SAG' STAGE CONTINUED

⟵ main transport direction of sediment

continental sands

prograding shelf sands

turbidites

shelf and reef limestones

shales and sands, sometimes deposited in oxygen deficient bottom conditions

Figure 8 Key stages in the rifting of continental crust and subsequent sea-floor spreading. Further explanation is given in the text.

(c)–(d) 'Sag' stage: movement along the faults initiated at the continental rift stage ceases, and the entire continental margin subsides (rather than subsidence being the result of movement of fault blocks) as the crust cools with increasing distance from the ridge-spreading axis as the ocean widens. The continental margin *progrades*^A laterally as *continental shelf*^A and *continental slope*^A sediments build upwards and outwards.

Important indicators of initial rifting and separation of continents include the association of basaltic igneous activity with the development of relatively narrow rift basins, which are followed by a more widespread regional subsidence or sag. This is referred to as a *rift-to-sag pattern*.

rift-to-sag pattern

This is not exclusively confined to continental margins, as will be discussed later in the Block. This pattern is also exhibited by intra-continental rifts that failed to develop as ocean spreading centres.

4.3 Vanished oceans

There are two ways in which the former presence of a wide ocean can be inferred, one of which was discussed in Section 2.

Can you recall what it was?

The construction of apparent polar wandering curves from palaeomagnetic studies of rocks reveals mismatches between such curves constructed from data acquired on different continents. These mismatches can be explained by invoking ocean opening, as for the Atlantic Ocean over the past 200 Ma, or by ocean closure as in the Atlantic area during the period between 500 and 390 Ma (see Figure 1, Section 2). Depending on the orientation of the former ocean, palaeomagnetic studies may give some indication of the former width of the ocean. (Remember, palaeomagnetic studies only yield data on palaeolatitudes, *not* palaeolongitudes.)

The second line of evidence indicating the former existence of a wide ocean comes from studies of fossil faunas. Assemblages on one side of an ocean may differ from those on the other, until it became very narrow or completely closed. The corollary of this is of course that separate continental masses with near identical terrestrial or freshwater fossil faunas must once have been united. We shall meet such examples later in the Block.

4.4 Subduction

In Blocks 3 and 4, the products of processes acting along subduction zones were discussed.

> Before reading on, try to recall the main features that can be preserved in the rock record as indicators of past episodes of subduction. List the indicators under the headings of: igneous (volcanic and intrusive); metamorphic; sedimentary; and structural.

Igneous rocks: The volcanic rocks formed at subduction zones range from *basalts*[A] through *andesites*[A] to *rhyolites*[A]. The key igneous indicator of subduction is the occurrence of andesite. As discussed in Block 3, andesite is produced either by the partial melting of ocean crust as it descends into the *mantle*[A] or by the dehydration and melting of the overlying mantle, followed in both cases by *fractional crystallization*[A]. These andesitic lavas rise to the surface to form *composite volcanoes*[A] at continental destructive margins, or *island arcs*[A] where one oceanic plate descends beneath another (see Block 3, Figure 37). Subduction associated with a continental destructive margin also results in the production of granitic *magmas*[A], either by melting of the crust in the presence of water, or at much greater depths via the fractional crystallization of basaltic or andesitic magmas. Dry granitic magma is capable of reaching the surface to be erupted as rhyolite, whereas wet magma is more likely to crystallize at depth as granite.

Metamorphic rock: The key metamorphic indicator of past subduction is the occurrence of *paired metamorphic belts*[A]. The downward moving ocean plate, being relatively cool at depth, is subjected to low temperature–high pressure metamorphism. In contrast, magmas generated by partial melting of the downgoing plate rise into the overriding plate, thus elevating crustal temperatures to produce high temperature metamorphism (see Block 3, Figure 101).

Sedimentary rock: As the continental shelves bordering destructive continental margins are relatively narrow, sedimentary material is likely to be rapidly transported from the source area into the *ocean trench*[A]. The trench-fill is dominated by *turbidite*[A] sediments, the composition of which includes components from the andesitic volcanic terrains of the nearby continent or island arc. These sediments, and any deep-sea sediments above the downgoing oceanic crust, are generally not consumed at the subduction zone, but accumulate as a sedimentary and tectonic *accretionary prism*[A].

As well as additions of sediments from the ocean trench region, the continental margin is thickened by igneous *underplating*[A] (as described in Block 3) and so rises due to isostatic uplift. This causes sediment to be shed by rivers towards the continental interior. Such sediments are often derived from newly exposed granite masses and they are referred to as *molasse* deposits (see Figure 9(a)) in the Alps (see Block 3, Section 14), where they post-date the main orogenic phase, and are in fact derived from granites of Variscan age.

Structure: Directly above the shallowest part of subduction zones, and forming the 'overriding' side of ocean trenches, there occur accretionary prisms. In these prisms, both oceanic sediments (i.e. sediments that accumulated on the downgoing oceanic crust) and trench sediments, and even some oceanic crust, are 'plastered' against the overriding plate. This 'tectonic accretion' results from the development of a series of thrusts, as oceanic crust plus the overlying deep-water sediments and some outer trench sediments are pushed beneath the active continental margin (see Figure 9b). As more material is inserted in this way, thrusts formed at an earlier stage are rotated so that they dip more steeply and may eventually appear to be *reverse*[A] faults. Movement along the faults continues as they are stacked up, and

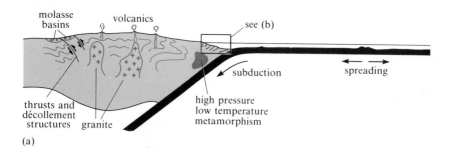

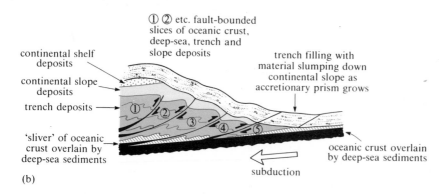

Figure 9 Subduction related features.

(a) Sketch section across a subduction zone involving continental crust showing key features discussed in the text.

(b) Sketch showing the principal features of an accretionary prism developed over a subduction zone. A series of thrust/fault-bounded slices of oceanic crust and sediment are produced as the downgoing plate carries material beneath the sedimentary-tectonic pile developing on the margin of the opposing plate. Thus as slice 5 is inserted, it alters the orientation of earlier slices (1–4), so that the older fault planes become more steeply inclined. Movement also continues on the older faults. Sedimentation is contemporaneous with the tectonic activity, with slumps and turbidity flows being triggered by the tectonic steepening of the trench slope.

moreover, sedimentation is contemporaneous with this tectonic activity. Sedimentary material is transported down the trench slope by slumping and *turbidity currents*[A], both of which may be triggered by the tectonic steepening of the slope. The end result of these tectonic and sedimentary processes is to produce the following features characteristic of a subduction zone:

A series of fault-bounded slices of sediments, beneath which may occur a sliver of oceanic crust (see ①–⑤ on Figure 9(b)).

The rocks of the sedimentary sequences *within* each fault slice are younger in the direction *opposite* to the movement of the downgoing plate. The sedimentary succession passes from deep-water deposits (*cherts*[A], black shales, carbonate *oozes*[A]) to trench, trench slope and shelf deposits.

The ages of the fault slices increase in the *same* direction as the movement of the downgoing plate (i.e. *away* from the trench).

The sediments may be *isoclinically folded*[A].

The orientation of the faulting changes from *low* angle near the trench, to *high* angle away from the downgoing plate.

In addition to structural developments in the immediate vicinity of ocean trenches, compressional movements may also affect the continental plate beyond the area of magmatic activity described earlier. This compression results in the development of thrusts as shown in Figure 9(a), and these structures may be contemporaneous with the development of the molasse basins described earlier.

4.5 Continental collision

The final closure of an ocean may bring together various combinations of the features described in the previous three sections. Basically former passive and destructive continental margins may be juxtaposed, or two destructive margins

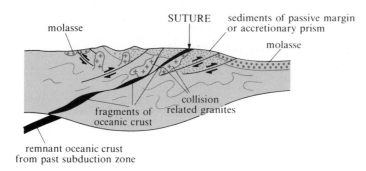

Figure 10 Sketch section across a continental collision zone, illustrating the location of most of the key features discussed in the text.

may collide with one another. In addition, former island arcs may be accreted onto a continental plate, as their density is low so that they cannot be subducted. Figure 10 shows most of the principal features developed by continental collision involving a former destructive and passive margin. The significant crustal thickening brought about by collision produces five significant features:

melting of continental crust to produce collision-related granites (Block 3, Section 8.2);

continued high temperature metamorphism;

deformation of earlier volcanic and sedimentary rocks to produce thrusts and fold axial planes inclined towards the suture zone.

isostatic uplift of the thickened crust may result in outward directed gravity sliding to produce *nappe*[A] structures similar to those of the Alps described in Block 3.

erosion of the newly uplifted mountain range results in the deposition of thick post-orogenic fluvial *sandstones*[A] (molasse).

The 'join' or suture between the two formerly separate continents may be marked by thrust slices of oceanic crust that failed to be subducted as collision occurred.

4.6 Summary

Table 2 summarizes the main indicators that can be used to help detect past oceanic and continental configurations. These indicators cannot be used to determine the former widths of an ocean. To a limited extent, palaeomagnetic and faunal studies can provide such information.

Table 2 Key features of continental separation, ocean closure and collision

	Igneous	Metamorphic	Sedimentary	Structural
Continental rifting and separation	Basaltic intrusives at rift stage. Oceanic crust sequence (basaltic pillow lavas underlain by dyke complex and gabbros and peridotites)	(You may have recalled the metamorphic facies zonation of oceanic crust (Block 3, Figure 33), but this is not important here)	Rift basins with fluvial, or restricted lake, marine or evaporitic sediments, followed by progradation of continental margin after separation (Figure 8)	'Rift to sag' trend: rifting followed by regional subsidence as crust cools as ocean spreading centre becomes more distant from margin
Ocean closure (subduction)	Andesitic volcanics and intrusives. Large granite intrusions on regional scale (Figure 9a)	Paired metamorphic belts (Figure 9a)	Development of accretionary prisms (Figure 9b)	
			Molasse basins initiated (Figure 9a)	Thrusting on continent beyond volcanic zone (Figure 9a)
Continental collision	Large granite intrusions on regional scale (Figure 10)	Regional high temperature metamorphism	Molasse basins (Figure 10)	Thrusts and fold axial planes inclined towards suture. Isostatic uplift and gravity sliding produces nappes

5 Precambrian Basement

5.1 Introduction

Although this Section dealing with the *Precambrian Basement* is quite short, you should be aware that it covers about three quarters of the time span of British rocks. Although much local detail is known about many of the outcrops, a considerable knowledge of regions outside the British Isles is needed to understand the early geological history of our region fully, and such coverage is beyond the scope of this Course.

The Basement is composed of rocks that are either *older* than those that make up the Caledonian Orogenic Belt, or they were left *unscathed by Caledonian events*. Figure 6 (Section 3.1) shows the distribution of the Basement rocks. Apart from those in the south-west of England (which will not be discussed until Section 7), geographically they fall into two groups: first, an extensive area in north-west Scotland and adjacent offshore regions, and second, scattered smaller outcrops in central England, north Wales and south-east Ireland. This geographical differentiation is paralleled by significant geological differences, as you will see shortly.

In Britain, the earliest radiometric dates from the Basement are around 2 700 Ma in the Lewisian of north-west Scotland, but it is not until around 1 000 Ma that a rock record is present in several separate regions. Thus, in this country, we cannot see rocks recording even earlier events in the Earth's history, shown on Figure 11 (the oldest rocks so far dated on the Earth are around 3 800 Ma, some 800 Ma short of the date of the origin of the Earth at 4 600 Ma). Caution is needed when interpreting the significance of radiometric dates—see Appendix.

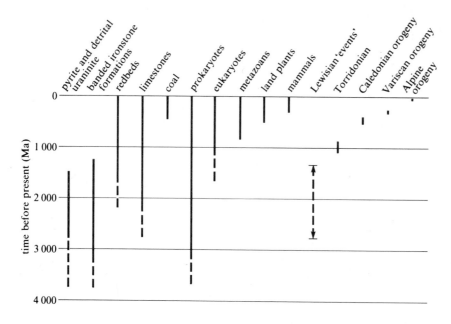

Figure 11 Some key events in the Earth's history, together with the major periods of earth movement affecting rocks of the British Isles.

4 600 – (formation of the Earth)

5.2 Scotland

Examine the Ten Mile Map (N) to the west of the Moine Thrust Zone in the area marked by the red rectangle labelled Assynt (NC(29)). List in chronological order the rock units that make up the Basement in this area. Note that the Moinian (10) is part of the Caledonian Orogenic Belt.

From the Ten Mile Map (N) it is possible to obtain the following information concerning the rocks of the Basement in north-west Scotland:

20

34	Granite intrusions	YOUNGEST
67	Durness *Limestone*[A]	Ordovician
63	Serpulite Grit and Fucoid Beds†	Cambrian
62	Pipe-Rock and Basal Quartzite†	
61	Sandstone and grit	Torridonian*
1	Undifferentiated *gneiss*[A] with dykes of basic rocks (5 and 6)	Lewisian OLDEST

* The Torridonian is not Palaeozoic in age as erroneously stated on the map Key, but Precambrian

† 'Fucoids' and 'Pipes' are *trace fossils*[A]

> How would you describe the nature of the contact between the Lewisian and Torridonian and between the Cambrian and the two older groups of rock? Look in square NC(29)11 and the red rectangle labelled Assynt.

Both contacts are unconformities. The dykes in the Lewisian (1) do not penetrate the Torridonian (61) (NC(29)11 and 12), and the Cambrian (62) rests on both Torridonian and Lewisian. Figure 12 is a structural sketch section across the area showing the relationships between these rock units and the location of the Moine metamorphic rocks above the Moine Thrust zone.

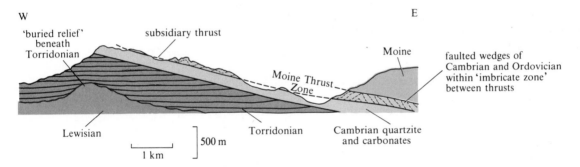

Figure 12 Sketch geological cross-section showing the structure of the Assynt region to the west of the Moine Thrust Zone. Note how Torridonian sediments mantle a palaeotopography developed over the Lewisian Complex and how Moine rocks (part of the Caledonian Orogenic Belt) are thrust over Basement composed of Lewisian, Torridonian and Cambrian–Ordovician rocks.

We can now briefly describe the geological history of this region as follows:

Lewisian events: radiometric dating has revealed two main metamorphic events at around 2 700 Ma and 1 850 Ma ago, and two phases of dyke intrusion at 2 200 Ma and 1 750 Ma ago. These episodes were part of more widespread orogenic and tensional events, which can be seen in Canada and Greenland.

Torridonian: red shales, *arkosic*[A] sandstones and *conglomerates*[A] laid down in fluvial and lake environments rest on an irregular surface of Lewisian showing a pre-Torridonian relief of up to 400 m. The lower part of the Torridonian has yielded radiometric dates of 995 ± 24 Ma, and the upper part 810 ± 175 Ma. It is probable that much of the Torridonian sediment was derived from sources in Greenland, which in its pre-drift position would have been adjacent to Scotland.

Cambrian–Ordovician sediments: after regional tilting of the Lewisian and Torridonian rocks (the Torridonian rocks are now horizontal because they were tilted back again after the Cambrian–Ordovician sediments were deposited), sediments were deposited on a relatively flat surface. These sediments are marine and accumulated in a shallow shelf environment, which became starved of siliciclastic sediment so that carbonates (*calcite*[A] and dolomite) of the Durness Limestones were deposited.

Thrusting resulted in the westward transport of the Moine metamorphic rocks during the Caledonian orogeny. Radiometric dates from the Moine give an Early Ordovician cooling age for the metamorphic rocks, thus indicating that a relatively short time (geologically speaking) elapsed between the deposition of the Durness Limestone and the final movement of the Moine Thrust Zone.

Two important points about the geology of north-west Scotland should be noted:

The Basement remained tectonically relatively stable from the last Lewisian metamorphic event at 1 850 Ma until the development of the Moine Thrust over 1 350 Ma later.

The Basement remained relatively unaffected by the Caledonian orogeny. The Moine rocks must have been metamorphosed at a location to the east and then thrust westwards.

5.3 England and Wales

There are several small outcrops of Basement in England and Wales, but as they are widely scattered and affected by the Caledonian orogeny, it is difficult to relate one to another. They consist of volcanic and thick sedimentary sequences. Volcanic rocks, especially rhyolites and andesites in Shropshire, south Wales and Leicestershire, and granitic intrusions in north and south Wales and Leicestershire yield ages mostly between 550 and 700 Ma so all the dates seem to be late Precambrian in age, so that the Basement is much younger than that of north-west Scotland. The presence of acidic and intermediate volcanics and intrusives points to an active continental/oceanic margin situated across the Midlands and Wales at this time. Indeed, there is evidence in Anglesey for a Late Precambrian–Early Cambrian subduction zone. Not surprisingly, the small amount of available information (limited by restricted outcrop) has led to a number of rival plate tectonic models. However, the majority of these favour an open ocean separating the English and Welsh region from the Basement area in Scotland. This postulated ocean is generally known as the *Iapetus Ocean* and was probably open during the late Precambrian. It later experienced subduction along its southern margin between about 700 and 550 Ma (i.e. before late Early Palaeozoic subduction and closure) causing the development of acidic and intermediate volcanics and intrusives. Although the debate concerning the plate tectonic interpretation of these English and Welsh rocks continues, there is no doubt that the geological development of north-west Scotland and of England and Wales was vastly different; this difference persisted throughout the development of the Caledonian Orogenic Belt.

Iapetus Ocean

The Basement of England and Wales is generally much younger than that of Scotland, and part of it (mostly in Wales) was deformed during the Caledonian orogeny. In contrast to the north-west Scottish area which remained a stable *cratonic*[A] area, the Anglo–Welsh area contains late Precambrian andesitic volcanics and granitic intrusions indicative of a nearby subduction zone; in Anglesey, late Precambrian and Early Cambrian rocks characteristic of such a zone are present.

6 The Caledonian Orogenic Belt

6.1 Introduction

Rocks deformed during the Caledonian orogeny are now widely separated on continents bordering the North Atlantic. By (mentally) closing the Atlantic, apparently disparate outcrops of rocks of similar type, structure and age can be joined into one belt, stretching from Scandinavia and Greenland, through the British Isles, and on into eastern North America, as shown in Figure 2, Section 2.

The rocks of the *Caledonian Orogenic Belt* are now generally accepted to be the result of depositional and volcanic events that occurred along the margin of a once wide ocean called Iapetus. These sediments and volcanics were later modified and augmented by processes associated with subduction along the margins of this ocean, until its closure, which was completed by the end of the Silurian.

Caledonian Orogenic Belt

As we saw earlier, palaeomagnetic data are consistent with this timetable of events. But what is the geological evidence for it, and in particular, what is the evidence for:

The former presence of a wide ocean?

Subduction along the margins of Iapetus?

The final closure of Iapetus, and the location of the suture along which once-separated continental masses were joined?

We shall answer these questions by searching for the 'indicators' discussed in Section 4 in each of the principal zones of the Caledonian orogeny in the British Isles, the locations of which are shown on Figure 13. This Figure shows the principal divisions of the Caledonides into metamorphic and non-metamorphic parts, with flanking cratonic areas to the north-west and south-east.

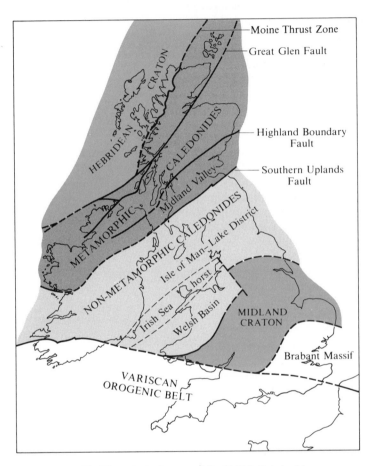

Figure 13   The principal zones of the British Caledonides.

6.2   The principal zones of the British Caledonides

6.2.1   Highlands

Examination of the Ten Mile Map (N) shows that much of the Highlands north-west of the Highland Boundary Fault consist of Moine (8–12) or Dalradian (13–25) metamorphic rocks intruded by granites (34). Much detailed mapping has been undertaken in the area, but its structural complexity is such that there is still much debate about the relationships between different rock units and tectonic structures. Figure 14 is a simplified structural sketch section across the region, which shows the contact between the Moine and Dalradian to be mostly tectonic (i.e. thrust) rather than stratigraphic in nature. Even a superficial examination of this sketch section reveals the extent of *crustal shortening*[A] in the region, and the similarities between the structure of the north-west Highlands and the idealized collision zone depicted in Figure 7.

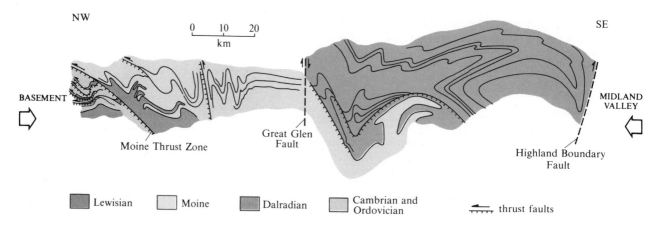

Figure 14 Sketch structural section showing the complex structures of the metamorphic Caledonides produced by crustal shortening. Note how the deformation patterns can be crudely interpreted in terms of 'squeezing' between the Basement to the north-west, and the Midland Valley region to the south-east; compare with Figures 9(a) and 10.

Moine

The Moine rocks are metamorphosed sediments that were deposited as a thick sequence (perhaps as much as 10 km) of sandstones and shales probably in a shallow marine environment. *Palaeocurrent directions*[A] show that sediment transport was towards the north and north-east. The western part of the Moine yields radiometric dates indicating a period of metamorphism at about 1 050 Ma, suggesting that the Moine suffered pre-Caledonian metamorphism, followed by further deformation during the Caledonian movements (see left side of Figure 14). However, it is not clear how much of the Moine sequence this early date can be applied to, and so the importance of the pre-Caledonian metamorphism is difficult to assess. Thus, if some part of the Moine was first metamorphosed some 1 050 Ma ago, it must have been deposited even earlier, and so must pre-date the Torridonian sediments. For this reason, it has been suggested that the orogeny affecting the Moine could be a continuation of an orogenic period between about 1 300 and 900 Ma ago seen in eastern Canada.

> If this is the case, what term would you apply to the Torridonian sediments? (Refer back to Table 2.)

The Torridonian sediments could therefore be molasse deposits following the orogeny. During the early Ordovician, the Moine rocks were thrust over the Lewisian, Torridonian and Cambro–Ordovician (see Figure 12, and the left side of Figure 14).

Dalradian

The Dalradian also consists of metamorphosed sediments indicative of a wide variety of surface environments, with metamorphosed volcanic rocks occurring at the top of the sequence, as shown in Figure 15. The total pre-deformation thickness of the Dalradian succession may have been as much as 20 km, but this is a cumulative thickness calculated by adding together the maximum thickness of each stratigraphic unit. It is most unlikely that such a thickness would accumulate at any single locality. The Dalradian is divided into four lithostratigraphic groups (Figure 15) and can be traced across Ireland and Scotland. The main features of these groups are described below: you are not expected to recall all the details, but you should remember the interpretation placed on these data.

The Grampian and Appin Groups contain *cross-bedding*[A], *ripple*[A] marks and fossil algal colonies (*stromatolites*[A]) indicative of marginal marine and shallow shelf environments. The base of the Argyll Group is marked by the Port Askaig Tillites, which are *matrix-supported*[A] conglomeratic sediments with large pebbles and cobbles which occasionally are striated. These sediments are now metamorphosed. Individual *tillite*[A] beds range between 0.5 and 65 m thick and may be traced laterally for 150 km across Ireland and Scotland. Some of the clasts (Block 4, Section 4.2.1) reach gigantic proportions, being up to 100 m long. The top of the tillites often show layers of sand and gravel, and sandstone-filled wedges often

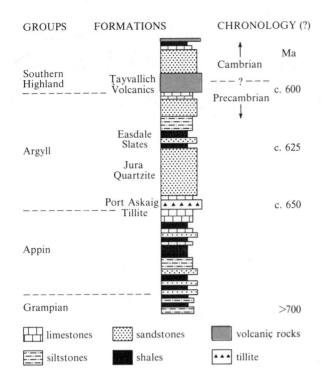

GROUPS   FORMATIONS   CHRONOLOGY (?)

| | limestones | | | sandstones | | | volcanic rocks |
| siltstones | | | shales | | | tillite |

Figure 15 The succession of rock units within the Dalradian. This is a composite section compiled from a variety of localities, and encompasses at least 10 km of strata.

penetrate them. All these features provide clear confirmation of the glacial origin of the sediments, and their exposure to later *periglacial conditions*[A], for the sandstone wedges are ancient analogues of ice wedges that today develop in such conditions, with the sands and gravels being deposited in them from melt-water streams. Comparable tillite units occur in the late Precambrian in Norway (where they have been dated at 668 ± 7 Ma), Sweden, Newfoundland, Greenland, and Spitsbergen. In Scandinavia, grooves gouged on rock surfaces indicate ice flow from the south-east, and in some Dalradian localities of Scotland, deformation caused by ice movements can be seen that suggest a similar ice flow from the south-east. The rock types exhibited by the clasts in the Scottish tillites cannot be matched with Basement rocks in north-west Scotland or Greenland, and so flow from the south-east also seems plausible on the basis of this negative evidence. The fact that evidence for ice sheets of the same age flowing to the north-west can also be seen on both sides of the postulated Iapetus Ocean (Scandinavia on its south-east side, Scotland on its north-west side) places a constraint on the time of opening of this ocean, because whereas icebergs could be imagined to have floated across Iapetus, icebergs today in open oceans are composed of debris-free ice, *and so incapable of producing thick* tills[A] *on melting*. Therefore it is probable that Iapetus opened *after* the major glacial period at approximately 670 Ma.

Above the tillites, much thicker sequences of metamorphosed sediments occur, indicating more rapid subsidence, with the former shallow subsiding shelf being broken into a series of fault bounded blocks and basins. This may signal the rifting phase that preceded the opening of Iapetus. Moreover, the coarser-grained sediments (now metamorphosed) at the top of the Argyll Group and in the Southern Highland Group contain features that indicate that they accumulated in *submarine fan*[A] environments such as by deposition along some kind of submarine slope. The Southern Highland Group has yielded Middle Cambrian *trilobites*[A] and *microfossils*[A] that suggest that the Cambrian–Precambrian boundary is somewhere within the top part of the Argyll Group or the base of the Southern Highland Group. The Southern Highland Group continues into the Early Ordovician. The lavas, dykes and *sills*[A] of the Tayvallich Volcanics indicate continued crustal extension, and may indicate the onset of sea-floor spreading.

This brief description of the sequence of events recorded in the Dalradian succession provides clues concerning the tectonic evolution of the area.

How does the change from a shallow, slowly subsiding shelf environment, to rapid subsidence of fault bounded basins, with later accompanying basaltic volcanism match with the generalized summary of tectonic plate and continental margin evolution given in Table 2 at the end of Section 4?

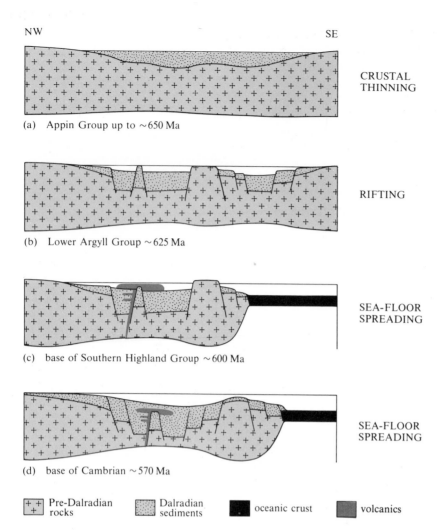

NW   SE

CRUSTAL THINNING

(a) Appin Group up to ~650 Ma

RIFTING

(b) Lower Argyll Group ~625 Ma

SEA-FLOOR SPREADING

(c) base of Southern Highland Group ~600 Ma

SEA-FLOOR SPREADING

(d) base of Cambrian ~570 Ma

| + +
 + | Pre-Dalradian rocks | | Dalradian sediments | | oceanic crust | | volcanics |

Figure 16 Sketch sections illustrating how the Dalradian succession may be interpreted in terms of continental rifting and the initiation of the Iapetus Ocean (compare with Figure 8).

As summarized in Figure 16, the Dalradian sequence can be interpreted in terms of a rifting phase in a continental region, which may have later led to the start of the ocean opening as signalled by the basaltic Tayvallich Volcanics. If this interpretation is correct, it indicates that the Iapetus Ocean did not exist at 670 Ma (on the basis of the tillite evidence), and began to open around 600 Ma, which is much later than the date suggested on the basis of studies of late Precambrian rocks in the English Midlands and Wales described in Section 5.3. However, these older Anglo–Welsh ocean indicators may be related to an older ocean.

Fairly soon after deposition, but after major deformation and metamorphism, the uppermost Dalradian sediments were intruded by basic igneous complexes, (27 on Ten Mile Map (N)) all dated at 480–514 Ma. Structural analysis indicates major NW–SE compression during the orogeny, which also caused the transport of material outwards along thrust planes to both the north-west and south-east, as is clearly shown on Figure 14. Later, at between 420 and 390 Ma, granite *plutons*[A] were intruded into the Highland region, and these are clearly visible on the Ten Mile Map; the significance of these will be discussed in Section 6.4.

Thus in a period of 100 Ma, the Highland area appears to have changed from a passive continental margin to an orogenic belt, as Iapetus first opened and then closed. But there is no clear evidence for the presence of a subduction zone and associated oceanic trench in the Highland area. Obviously, we should look for this to the south, in the Midland Valley or Southern Uplands region.

Our studies of the Dalradian so far provide the following clues concerning the evolution of the Caledonides on the north-west flank of the Iapetus Ocean:

The north-westerly flow of the ice sheet that deposited the Dalradian tillites suggests that Iapetus could not have existed at about 670 Ma.

Faulting contemporaneous with sedimentation indicates a period of crustal instability during the deposition of the Argyll Group and Southern Highland Group.

(This may be comparable to the rifting stage of ocean opening illustrated in Figure 8, top.) The Tayvallich Volcanics may indicate the initiation of sea-floor spreading in the Iapetus Ocean at around 600 Ma (Figure 8, middle stages).

Intense folding, thrusting and metamorphism may indicate continental collision at 500 Ma.

As there are only minor outcrops of Lower Palaeozoic rocks in the Midland Valley, we will examine next the Southern Uplands.

6.2.2 Southern Uplands

Figure 17 shows the outcrops of Ordovician and Silurian rocks in the Southern Uplands.

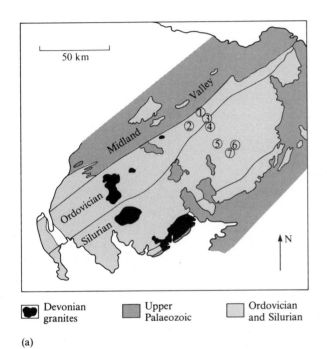

(a)

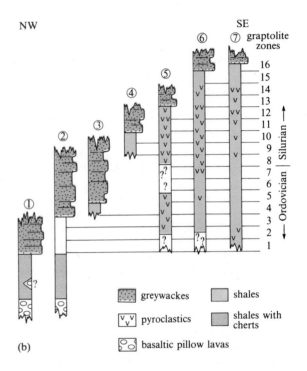

(b)

ITQ 21 Examine these areas as depicted on the Ten Mile Map (N). In which direction are the rocks 'younging' in the Southern Uplands? Does this 'younging' direction indicate a simple regional dip, or can you see evidence of any complex folding? Pay particular attention to the boundary beween 70–1 and 72 in Squares NX(25) 46, 47, 57 and 58.

ITQ 22 The Lake District map shows a generalized vertical succession of the lithological sequence in the southern part of the Southern Uplands, labelled SW Scotland. Give a brief description of this sequence.

Figure 17 The Ordovician and Silurian of the Southern Uplands. (a) Outcrop map of the Ordovician and Silurian in Scotland, showing localities of successions within the fault block illustrated in (b). See text for discussion.

So the outcrop pattern on the Ten Mile Map is deceptively simple. There is an overall younging to the south-east (as there is also in the Highlands of Scotland), but detailed mapping shows that isoclinical folding is present.

Lithological sequences in the Southern Uplands often show basalt overlain by relatively thin cherts (fine-grained beds of amorphous silica) and/or black shales, containing *graptolites*[A] which are followed by extremely thick sequences of greywackes deposited as turbidites.

ITQ 23 What kind of depositional environments did these sediments form in?

Studies of temporary exposures in gas pipeline trenches have shown that the Southern Uplands area is cut by a number of large faults. The sedimentary sequence within each fault block is significantly different, either in lithology, or age, or both, from its neighbours. Figure 17 shows the differences between the succession in each fault block. In general, *within* each fault block the strata dip at high

27

angles to the north-west and young mostly in the same direction, although there is some isoclinal folding present. This younging direction is the opposite to that observed across the *entire* Southern Uplands. This difference in younging direction is an important clue in deciphering how the succession in the area was formed. It must be stressed that the vertical scale on Figure 17(b) represents time and not thickness. Each graptolite zone probably spans about 3 Ma (assuming the Late Ordovician and Early Silurian are equivalent to a 50 Ma span of time). As far as thickness of the rock types are concerned, the greywackes may be several kilometres thick, whereas the chert, shales and *pyroclastic rocks*[A] are at the most 80 m thick.

> What do you notice about the age of the greywacke sequences between the different fault blocks (columns 1 – 7, Figure 17). Is there any systematic change in age from north-west to south-east?

The greywacke sequences are younger to the south-east—in the case of fault blocks numbers ③ and ④, the difference is as much as six graptolite zones, which may represent a period of 18 Ma. Thus it seems likely that the sequences were originally deposited some distance from one another. So in the Southern Uplands, a picture emerges of a series of NE–SW trending fault slices *within* which the strata are steeply dipping and sometimes folded and generally young to the north-west, but the *regional* younging direction (that seen on the Ten Mile Map) is to the south-east. The age of onset of greywacke sedimentation also diminishes towards the south-east.

Perhaps by now you have recognized the nature of this assemblage of sedimentary and tectonic features. If not, look back to Table 2 at the end of Section 4. All these features are characteristic of an accretionary prism developed over a subduction zone. A generalized accretionary prism model was shown in Figure 9 (Section 4.4). It is probable that the belt of Ordovician and Silurian rocks in the Southern Uplands represents an accretionary prism that formed over a subduction zone as the Iapetus Ocean closed. In such a model, the black graptolitic shales and cherts represent ocean-floor sediments, and greywackes represent trench and slope deposits. Thrusting associated with subduction began towards the end of the Ordovician and continued into the Silurian (Figure 18), producing a series of thrust sheets showing a northward increase in thrust/fault inclination. The Southern Uplands Fault represents the northern limit of this accretionary prism. As the prism developed, parts of it rose above sea-level to form land, which shed sediments to the south and also to the north, as evidenced by Silurian exposures in the Hagshaw Hills, 30 km south of Glasgow (see outcrop of 72–4 in squares NS(26)63 and 73. To the north of the western termination of the Southern Uplands Fault, around Ballantrae (square NX(25)0982), the Ordovician also consists of greywackes (HEK Specimen 12(M) came from here) underlain by basalt, but in addition, gabbros and *ultrabasic rocks*[A] occur and suggest that the sequence is a slice of oceanic crust and associated sediments (labelled ophiolite on Figure 19 and elsewhere). It is possible that this slice of oceanic crust was pushed up (instead of being subducted downward as in the accretionary prism area to the south) at the end of the Early Ordovician. Indeed, some workers believe that this is evidence in favour of a two-stage opening and closing cycle for the Iapetus Ocean, with the first closure at about 500 Ma producing the Highland metamorphism and deformation, and the second the Southern Uplands accretionary prism.

accretionary prism model for the Southern Uplands

Figure 18 An accretionary prism model for the Ordovician and Silurian of the Southern Uplands. The major faults defining the fault blocks (the locations of ①–⑦ are shown in Figure 17a) become steeper away from the postulated ocean trench.

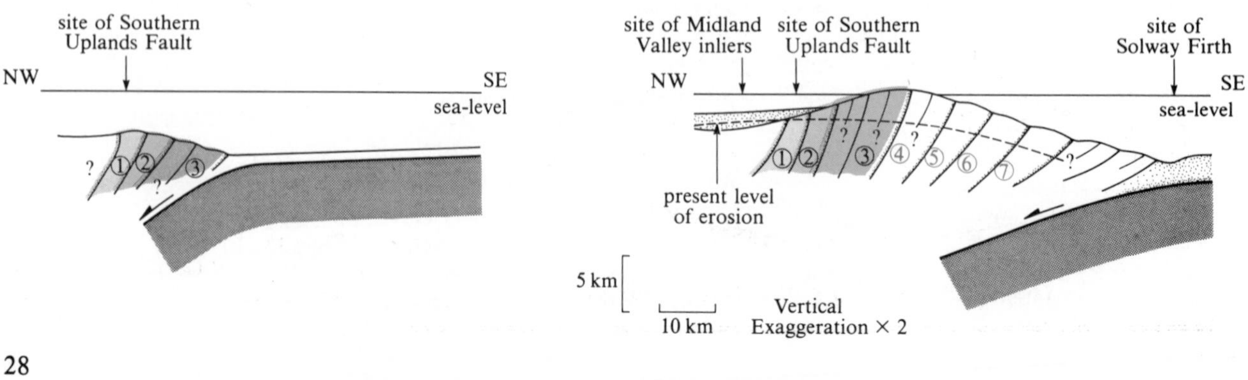

The story so far: the development of the northern margin of Iapetus.

It seems that the Dalradian sequences record the opening of the Iapetus Ocean, with the Tayvallich Volcanics signalling the beginning of sea-floor spreading far to the south in Early Cambrian times. Subduction and the formation of an accretionary prism occurred in the Southern Uplands area during Ordovician and Early Silurian times. South of the Highland Boundary Fault, no Cambrian sediments are exposed in Scotland, so there is no record of events for this interval. The evolutionary model we favour is illustrated in Figure 19. You should realize that several variant models have been proposed and doubtless more will be proposed in the future.

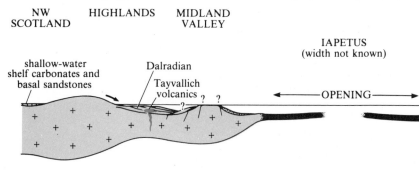

EARLY CAMBRIAN ~ 570 Ma

EARLY ORDOVICIAN ~ 490 Ma

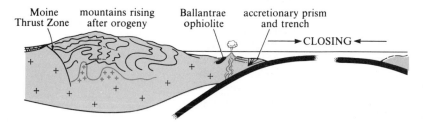

LATE ORDOVICIAN ~ 440 Ma

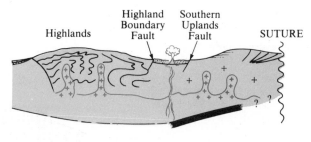

END SILURIAN/EARLY DEVONIAN ~ 395 Ma

Figure 19 Evolutionary model for the development of the northern margin of the Iapetus Ocean.

6.2.3 Lake District

ITQ 24   Using the Lake District geological map, compare the Lake District and Southern Uplands areas by answering the following questions. The first two questions posed below can be answered by examining the vertical sections.

(a) Are the sedimentary sequences in the two areas similar?

(b) Are the igneous rocks in the two areas similar?

(c) Does the structure of the Lake District suggest the presence of a series of fault blocks similar to those that are seen in the Southern Uplands? Answer this question by examining the cross-sections.

Answer these questions by completing the table:

	Lake District	Southern Uplands
Sedimentary sequences		
Igneous rocks		
Structure		

The most striking difference between the Lake District and the Southern Uplands is the occurrence of a thick series of *andesitic volcanic rocks* (the Borrowdale Volcanic Group) and the apparent absence of reverse faulting and isoclinal folding. Thus, whereas there is no evidence for the development of an accretionary prism in the Lake District, the presence of andesitic volcanic rocks indicates that the area was situated above a subduction zone. And, given that we have a northward dipping subduction zone in the Southern Uplands with an ocean situated to the south, it seems logical to assume that the andesitic volcanics in the Lake District indicate subduction on the southern margin of the Iapetus Ocean. So now we have evidence that subduction was occurring on both the southern and northern margins of Iapetus during the Early to Middle Ordovician. In contrast to the Southern Uplands, however, there is no definite evidence in the rocks of the Lake District for subduction to have continued into the Silurian, although this cannot be ruled out.

6.2.4   Wales and the Midlands

As discussed in Section 5.3, this area contains evidence for an earlier phase of plate collision during the late Precambrian, in that the Palaeozoic sections in the area are underlain by metamorphic rocks, as exposed in Anglesey, and by volcanic rocks and Precambrian sediments in Shropshire and Leicestershire. Figure 20 illustrates the main palaeogeographic elements of the region during the Lower Palaeozoic, and summarizes the rock succession that is encountered in each area.

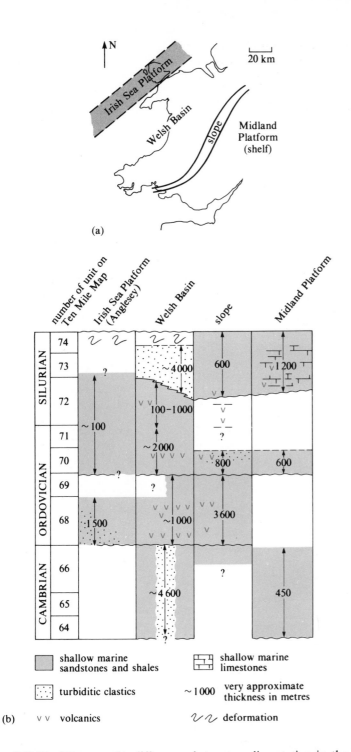

Figure 20 The Lower Palaeozoic of Wales.
(a) Main palaeogeographic elements of
Wales and the English Midlands during the
Lower Palaeozoic. (b) Lower Palaeozoic
successions typical of each area shown in
(a).

ITQ 25 What are the differences between sedimentation in the Welsh
Basin and over the Irish Sea Platform and Midland Platform? Consider (a)
the presence of discontinuities in the rock record (b) contrasts in thickness,
and (c) the nature of the sediments.

Irish Sea Platform

This is an area that remained relatively high during the subsidence of the flanking
areas during the Lower Palaeozoic. In Anglesey, Ordovician conglomerates and
sandstones (>1 000 m) rest unconformably on late Precambrian and Early Cambrian subduction-related basement rocks, and are succeeded unconformably by
100 m of Late Ordovician and Early Silurian shales.

Welsh Basin

A very thick sequence (>10 000 m) of Lower Palaeozoic sediments occurs, with
significant Lower Ordovician acidic and intermediate volcanics (pre-dating those
of the Lake District) present both in north Wales (see Colour Plate 6.1) and south
Wales, and another later Ordovician volcanic episode post-dating that in the Lake

District. In West Dyfed (Pembrokeshire), Silurian volcanism is also important. It seems that going south from the Lake District to south Wales, volcanism may have ended at successively later periods. The sediments consist largely of muds (now *slates*[A]) containing graptolites, and turbidites containing shallow shelf types of fauna. This assemblage of sediments containing faunas indicative of both deep-water and shallow-water conditions was brought together by successive turbidity flows on submarine fans building into the basin from the north-west and south-east at various times. Figure 21 shows the distribution of these turbidite/fan sediments during the Early Silurian; an earlier fan building episode occurred during the Cambrian. The rapid subsidence rates, which permitted such thick sequences to accumulate, and the occurrence of major slumped horizons suggest that faulting during deposition exerted a considerable control on sedimentation in some areas, particularly on and adjacent to the slope bordering the Midland Platform.

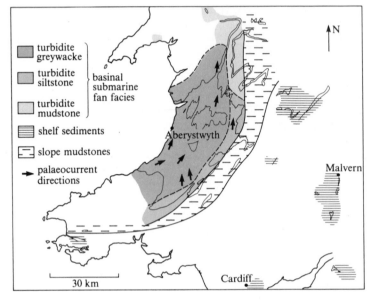

Figure 21 Map showing the distribution of rock types and sedimentary environments during the Upper Llandovery (unit 72 on the Ten Mile Map).

Midland Platform

This was an area that was either mostly *emergent* or only very slowly subsiding, for over it accumulated relatively thin shallow-water shelf types of sediment (see Colour Plate 6.2), often containing stratigraphic breaks (see Figure 21 for the extent of the shelf during the early Silurian). The slope between the platform and the Welsh Basin was probably located along a zone that today exhibits important faults (see NE–SW trending Church Stretton Fault on the Ten Mile Map (S) from SJ(33)7016 to SO(32)2354). The south-eastward extent of this platform is known only from borehole records such as the Lower Lemington borehole shown on the Moreton-in-Marsh map. The Midland Platform is therefore the southern counterpart of the shelf in north-west Scotland that bordered the opposite margin of the Caledonian Belt.

It is generally accepted that Lower Palaeozoic deposition in Wales and the Midlands occurred in a fault-controlled basin or basins separated from the Iapetus Ocean by a *horst*[A]-like area—the Irish Sea Platform. To the north-west of this horst, in the Isle of Man and the Lake District, thick sedimentary sequences were deposited that may have formed on the continental slope and shelf flanking the open ocean or in a basin situated behind an island arc.

But there is no analogue of the Southern Uplands accretionary prism, and so subduction can only be inferred, but not precisely located, by the occurrence of the acid and intermediate volcanic rocks in the Lake District and north and south Wales. Earth movements affected the sequences in the Early Ordovician and again in the Late Ordovician, with the major phase of deformation occurring at the end of the Silurian. Post-orogenic molasse deposits of Devonian Old Red Sandstone were deposited unconformably over the deformed Lower Palaeozoic rocks.

	landmass; shoreline uncertain
	Iapetus (width not to scale)
▲	volcanics
	Old Red Sandstone

(Part of Figure 22, see caption opposite.)

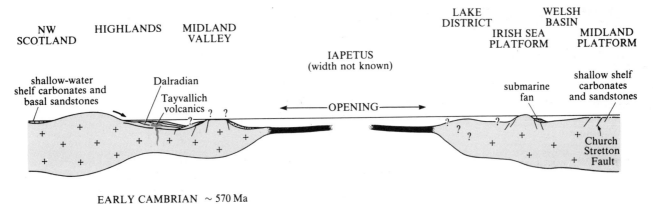

NW
SCOTLAND   HIGHLANDS   MIDLAND
VALLEY

LAKE   WELSH
DISTRICT   BASIN
IRISH SEA   MIDLAND
PLATFORM   PLATFORM

IAPETUS
(width not known)

shallow-water
shelf carbonates and   Dalradian
basal sandstones

Tayvallich
volcanics   ? ?

OPENING

submarine
fan

shallow shelf
carbonates
and sandstones

Church
Stretton
Fault

EARLY CAMBRIAN ~ 570 Ma

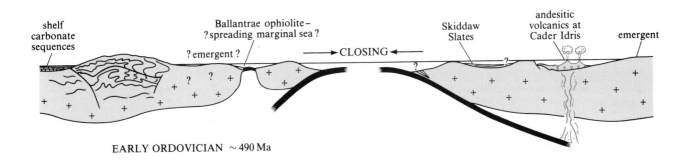

shelf
carbonate
sequences

Ballantrae ophiolite –
?spreading marginal sea ?

? emergent ?   CLOSING

Skiddaw
Slates

andesitic
volcanics at
Cader Idris   emergent

EARLY ORDOVICIAN ~ 490 Ma

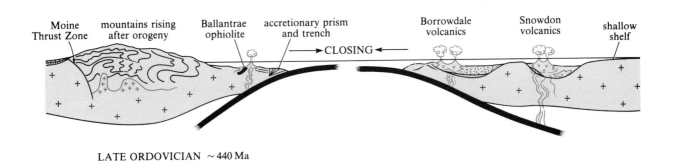

Moine
Thrust Zone

mountains rising
after orogeny

Ballantrae
ophiolite

accretionary prism
and trench   CLOSING

Borrowdale
volcanics

Snowdon
volcanics   shallow
shelf

LATE ORDOVICIAN ~ 440 Ma

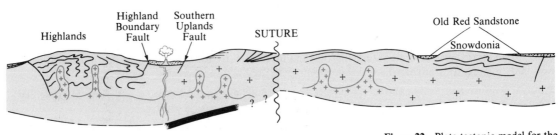

Highlands

Highland   Southern
Boundary   Uplands
Fault   Fault

SUTURE

Old Red Sandstone

Snowdonia

END SILURIAN/EARLY DEVONIAN ~ 395 Ma

Figure 22 Plate tectonic model for the development of the British Caledonides.

6.3   The site of the Iapetus suture

Iapetus suture

We have now virtually completed our tour of the Caledonides in Britain. We have seen that there is evidence for subduction of the Iapetus Ocean northwards, beneath the Southern Uplands, and southwards beneath the Lake District and Wales. Thus it is reasonable to assume that the suture along which the two formerly separate continental masses were joined must occur somewhere in the Solway Firth area. This conclusion is reinforced by studies of trilobites and *bra-chiopods*[A], which show that those of the Pacific faunal *province*[A] are found north of the suture, and those of the Atlantic province to the south.

6.4 Post-orogenic granites

Examination of the Ten Mile Map (N) shows that a major part of the Caledonian terrain is intruded by granites, which in places have cross-cutting relations to Caledonian structures; this is particularly obvious in the Southern Uplands.

> From the evidence available on the Ten Mile Maps and the Lake District map, are post-orogenic granites confined to the area north of the Iapetus suture?

No, they also occur in the Lake District.

Geophysical and borehole evidence has shown that such granites also occur beneath the Carboniferous rocks in the northern Pennines. The radiometric ages of the granites cluster around 400 Ma making them Early Devonian in age, indicating that they were intruded after subduction had ceased.

> Is the timing of these granite intrusions consistent with the subduction model for the Caledonides illustrated in Figure 9(a)?

The granites do not appear to be related to active subduction zones. It is possible that granite magma was generated as a result of crustal thickening and the consequent subjection of continental crust to higher temperatures (Block 3, Section 13.3.1); in other words the granites are probably 'collision related' as illustrated on Figure 10.

6.5 Summary

Figure 22 provides a pictorial summary of the evolution of the Caledonian orogeny in the British Isles region. Once again, we must stress that this is just one plate tectonic model for the Caledonides and that several other variations have been and will be proposed.

7 Older Cover and Variscan Orogenic Belt

7.1 Introduction

In this Section, we will consider the Late Palaeozoic evolution of the British Isles, save that the Permian is discussed in a later Section, as sediments laid down at this time form part of the Younger Cover. The Devonian and Carboniferous terrains in the British Isles can be divided into two parts:

Older Cover: relatively undeformed sediments (but on a local scale strong deformation may be present) overlying the Caledonian Orogenic Belt.

Variscan Orogenic Belt: sediments and some volcanics deformed during the Variscan* orogeny towards the end of the Carboniferous, and somewhat earlier in south Cornwall.

These tectonic divisions, and those we have already examined, of the British stratigraphic column into the two orogenic periods and the Older and Younger Covers are somewhat arbitrary, because there are many examples of transitional boundaries. Thus as we shall see, the closing events of the Caledonian orogeny affect the overlying Older Cover in places, and Variscan earth movements, though

---

* Unfortunately three different names are used in Europe to denote late Palaeozoic orogenic events; in addition to the term Variscan, you may find the terms Armorican and Hercynian used from time to time in other literature. Because the Hercynian refers to the direction of folds in the Harz region of Germany, and the Armorican to that in Armorica (an old name for Brittany), Variscan, which has no directional implication, is preferred.

confined mainly to south-west England and south Wales, also affect other areas to the north to a lesser extent.

In the exercise below, you will use the evidence presented on the Ten Mile Map to explore some aspects of the Older Cover and Variscan Orogenic Belt.

ITQ 26   Answer the following questions by examining the two Ten Mile Map sheets (and, where indicated, the Lake District, Moreton-in-Marsh and Cheddar sheets). Look in turn at each of the areas numbered 1 to 12 on Table 3, and indicate (use a tick) in the Table:

(a) which units of the Carboniferous are present in each area;

(b) which parts of the Devonian/Old Red Sandstone are present in each area;

(c) whether volcanic activity of Devonian or Carboniferous age is present in each area.

Table 3   For use with ITQ 26

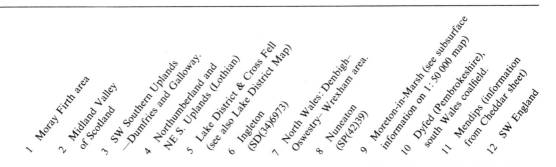

(a) CARBONIFEROUS

84 Westphalian &
   Stephanian:

82–3 Westphalian
   (mainly 'Coal
   Measures')

81 Namurian
   (Millstone Grit)

80 Tournaisian &
   Viséan
   (Carboniferous
   Limestone
   Series)

(b) DEVONIAN/O.R.S.

78 Upper Old Red
   Sandstone

   Devonian
   Limestone

75 Lower Old Red
   Sandstone

(c) VOLCANIC ACTIVITY

49–52 Devonian
   Volcanics

53–55 Carboniferous
   Volcanics

Whilst completing Table 3, you have collected data relevant to the following general points concerning the development of the Older Cover.

If you compared the keys on the two Ten Mile Maps, you will have noticed that the term *Old Red Sandstone* is used on the north sheet, but on the south one, it is used in conjunction with Devonian. This is because Devonian sediments in south-west England are developed mostly in a marine facies, whereas to the north they are

Old Red Sandstone

35

almost entirely continental, and referred to as the Old Red Sandstone though they are also of Devonian age.

The Middle Old Red Sandstone (77) is only developed extensively in the Moray Firth area and the Orkneys and Shetland. This region is called the Orcadian Basin; elsewhere the Middle Devonian is not represented in the rock record, except by the marine sequence of south-west England. This absence indicates either a period of non-deposition or that if Middle Devonian deposits were formed, they were later eroded away.

A glance at your completed version of Table 3 shows that the Old Red Sandstone is missing in places over the Southern Uplands (except in the north-east) and over the Lake District and northern Pennine areas. This suggests that these regions were either emergent during the Devonian, or if Old Red Sandstone sediments were deposited, they were stripped off following uplift before deposition of Carboniferous sediments. The Old Red Sandstone is absent in north Wales (except in Anglesey), but appears in south Wales. This suggests continued uplift of this part of the Caledonian Orogenic Belt in Devonian times.

Your completed Table 3 will show that the Carboniferous is much more widespread than the Devonian. The Upper Carboniferous rests directly on the Lower Palaeozoic at several localities in the Southern Uplands, and in the Midlands (Nuneaton, Moreton), it also rests on Lower Palaeozoic. So, in these areas, the Lower Carboniferous is entirely absent. This suggests another emergent area existed during Early Carboniferous times; it is usually called *St George's Land* (see also later discussion in Section 7.2.5).   **St George's Land**

During the Devonian and Carboniferous, volcanic activity is largely confined to the Midland Valley of Scotland and the far north of England. Less extensive volcanic activity occurred in Derbyshire during the Lower Carboniferous (and can be seen on the Ten Mile Map) and also in the marine Devonian and Carboniferous sediments of Cornwall.

From the evidence you have just collated from the Ten Mile Map, it is possible to reach three important conclusions concerning the events that contributed to the formation of the Older Cover:

Significant parts of the British Isles either were land areas experiencing erosion during the Devonian, or were the sites of accumulation of continental sediments (the Old Red Sandstone);

During the Carboniferous, particularly during Late Carboniferous times, many parts of the former Devonian land areas were mantled by sediment.

Significant volcanic activity occurred during both the Devonian and the Carboniferous in the Midland Valley of Scotland and in Northumberland.

Why should there have been extensive land areas in Britain during the Devonian?

Continental collision occurred between what is now northern England and the Southern Uplands at the end of the Silurian, and related earth movements and the intrusion of collision-related granites continued into the early Devonian (see Figure 22). The resultant crustal thickening and consequent isostatic uplift accounts for the extensive Devonian land areas. Indeed, much of Wales, northern England and Scotland were mountainous regions at this time, comparable in relief to the present-day Alps.

The Old Red Sandstone is an example of a particular kind of sedimentation that follows an episode of mountain building. Can you recall the general name given to such sediments? (Look at Figures 9 and 10.)

The Old Red Sandstone is a good example of a molasse deposit that accumulated in basins within (e.g. Moray Firth and Midland Valley), and marginal to (e.g. Wales) a newly formed orogenic belt.

By the Carboniferous, the relief of the Caledonian mountains had been reduced to sea-level over considerable areas by erosion, and so it is not suprising that sediments of this age occur over a wider area than those of the Devonian.

In addition, a global sea-level rise or *marine transgression*[A], occurred at the beginning of the Carboniferous causing an enlargement of the depositional areas.

The origin of the large amounts of volcanic rocks within the Older Cover of northern areas is discussed later in this Section.

We have not yet identified the nature of the structures characteristic of the Variscan orogeny.

> **ITQ 27**   Describe the nature of the folding (e.g. symmetry, axial trends) in Upper Palaeozoic strata at the following localities on the Ten Mile Map (S):
>
> (a) The tract of country north of St Govan's Head (SR(11)9793)
>
> (b) South Wales coalfield and the Gower Peninsula (which is north-east of Worms Head SS(21)4087).
>
> (c) The Forest of Dean (just east of Monmouth, in squares SO(32) 50, 51, 60, 61) and in the Bristol area to the south.
>
> (d) Mendips (use the data you have on the Cheddar Sheet).
>
> (e) South-west England (Devon and Cornwall).

From the simple structural analysis you have just completed, it should be clear that the Variscan deformation was caused by northward directed compressional movements. Not only are many of the anticlinal folds you have examined asymmetrical, with steeper northern limbs, including overthrusting to the north in the Mendips, but the intensity of the deformation increases to the south.

To the north of the Variscan Orogenic Belt, structures often follow trends in the underlying Caledonian basement. The north–south folding in the Bristol and Forest of Dean areas may reflect structures in the Caledonian basement, and further to the north-west between Brecon (SO(32)0528) and Builth Wells (SO(32)0450), it is possible to see on the Ten Mile Map that the Old Red Sandstone has been folded along a NE–SW Caledonian-type trend. It is worth tracing the outcrop of Devonian strata from south-west Wales into central Wales, for in this direction you can see how it changes from a characteristic E–W Variscan trend to a NE–SW trend.

7.2   Older Cover

7.2.1   Devonian molasse

Older Cover

We have already concluded that the Old Red Sandstone is an example of a post-orogenic molasse deposit. What would the Devonian landscape over much of the British Isles have looked like? Colour Plate 6.3 is an artist's impression of such a landscape. But how do we know that rivers flowed from the Caledonian landscape to deposit the Old Red Sandstone, and how do we know that the conditions were rather arid? As you saw in Block 4, the nature of past sedimentary environments can be interpreted by considering *all* the features of sedimentary sequences.

Figure 23 shows four lithological *graphic logs*[A] of Old Red Sandstone sequences from the Midland Valley of Scotland and from Dyfed in Wales.

> Can you see any pattern to the grain size distributions on the logs?

There is an alternation of *suspension deposits*[A] (mudstones and siltstones) and *traction deposits*[A] (the sands and conglomerates), and in many cases the latter show a fining upward trend in grain size.

> In columns (a) and (d) you should be able to spot a repetition of trends in the type of sedimentary structures present, and interpret this, together with the grain size trends, in terms of changing current conditions.

In columns (a) and (d), the fining upward trend in grain size is accompanied by changes in the type of sedimentary structure present, from large-scale cross-bedding (the base contains pebbles and erodes into the underlying silts), to *planar bedding*[A], to small-scale cross-bedding. These features are a clear indicator of an

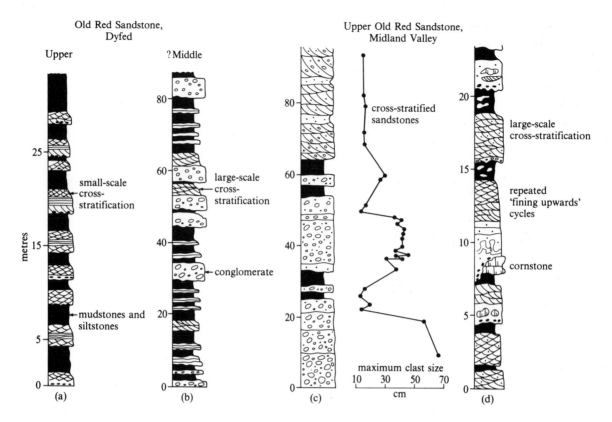

Figure 23 Old Red Sandstone sedimentary sequences. Note that the width of the columns is roughly proportional to grain size and that the scales of the various columns are not identical. For explanation see text.

upward decrease in current velocity culminating in the deposition of the silts as suspension deposits.

Can you recall from Block 4 how this assemblage of features is interpreted?

This assemblage is characteristic of deposits laid down by *meandering*[A] rivers. So we have good evidence for fluvial deposition of the Old Red Sandstone. Do the other columns (b) and (c) fit into this interpretation? Column (b) shows conglomeratic sediments, some of which fine upwards into cross-bedded sands, plus cross-bedded and flat-bedded sands, all of which are interbedded with silts. This sequence suggests that deposition occurred on an *alluvial fan*[A].

How would you interpret the top part of column (c), from 62 m up, in terms of the fluvial models presented in Block 4?

This part of column (c) was deposited by *braided rivers*[A], whereas the conglomeratic lower part, in which the clasts are poorly *sorted*[A] and set in a fine-grained *matrix*[A], were laid down by mudflows resulting from sudden storms rapidly transporting and quickly dumping material. There were a wide variety of fluvial environments present during the deposition of the Old Red Sandstone. But what are the grounds for our earlier statement that the environment was also arid? Apart from the fact that the sequences are very similar to fluvial deposits forming in present-day arid regions (as shown in TV 11), two particular features of the sediments indicate aridity. One is their red colour, produced by the oxidation of *ferromagnesian minerals*[A] in the sediments; had they been deposited in an environment that remained waterlogged (as in many temperate and tropical river systems), this oxidation would not have occurred. Secondly, the cornstones shown on Figure 23 (d), which are very common in the Old Red Sandstone, are fossil soils of a type that today only form in arid regions. The cornstones range from fine-grained nodular to unbedded limestone which has *replaced* and *displaced* the surrounding siliciclastic sediments.

Similar features form in present-day *deserts*[A], as pore waters within fluvial sediments are evaporated, causing the precipitation of calcite, which displaces the individual grains, and corrodes them.

Integration of the kind of detailed studies outlined above with knowledge of the distribution of Devonian sediments enables a sketch map of *Devonian palaeogeography* to be prepared of the kind shown in Figure 24. The evidence for the reconstruction of conditions in the south-west England area will be discussed later, in Section 7.3.2.

Devonian palaeogeography

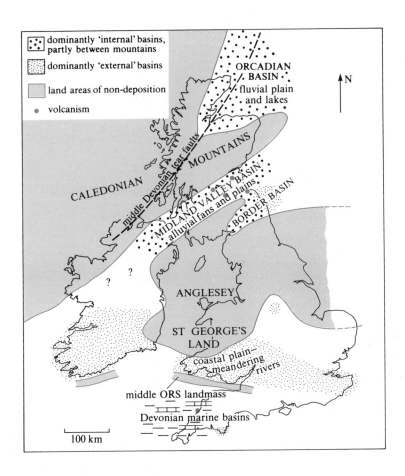

Figure 24 Palaeogeographic sketch map for the Devonian of the British Isles. Fluvial sediments were deposited both within the Caledonian mountains and to the south of them where coastal plains bordered the Devonian sea, which extended eastwards into France and Germany.

7.2.2 The Carboniferous transgression

In completing Table 3, you observed that sediments of Early Carboniferous age are more widespread than those of Devonian age, and we commented that this was largely a result of a transgression. Thus, in many places in Britain, continental Old Red Sandstone is overlain by marine strata that are termed the Carboniferous Limestone Series. From general knowledge, and viewing TV 3 and 4 on Ingleton and Cheddar, you probably have gained the impression that the Carboniferous Limestone Series is typified by thickly bedded, well jointed grey limestones. In fact, the unit labelled Carboniferous Limestone Series (80) on the Ten Mile Map consists of a great variety of rock types as you can see by looking at Figure 25. But

Figure 25 Lower Carboniferous successions illustrating changes of thickness, facies and age between the Basins and Blocks shown in Figure 26. For the purpose of answering ITQ 28, you can assume that the parts of the succession with corresponding labels 1–6 are time equivalent.

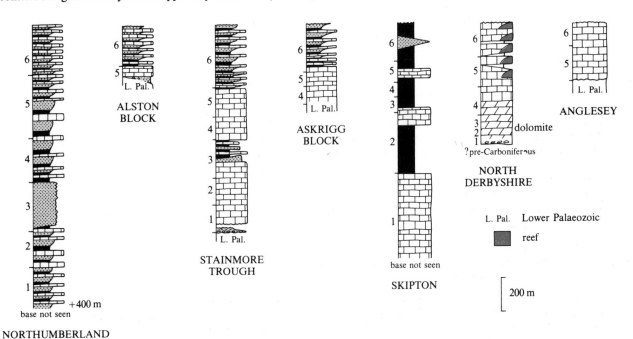

first let us ignore the lithological variety, and consider the age of the base of the Carboniferous Limestone Series, or what we will now call Lower Carboniferous*.

> **ITQ 28** Identify the relative ages of the *oldest* Lower Carboniferous strata at each locality as shown on Figure 25, and decide whether the Early Carboniferous transgression was abrupt or gradual. The localities are arranged in north–south order, but at this point you need not be aware of their precise locations. The numbers on the side of each column are equivalent to the *biostratigraphic*[A] divisions of the successions; in other words, they refer to approximate 'time slices' of the successions. You may use them to correlate the successions and indicate the relative age of their bases.

Thus the remnants of the old Caledonian highlands were gradually transgressed during the Early Carboniferous.

7.2.3 Blocks and basins

Figure 26 depicts the thickness changes of Carboniferous strata along a north–south section from the Midland Valley to St George's Land. It shows that certain areas subsided much more rapidly than others. Thus in the *basins* or *troughs*, relatively thick and complete Carboniferous successions occur, whereas over the regions that did not subside so rapidly (the *blocks*), relatively thin and incomplete successions are present. You have already seen from examining Figure 25 (ITQ 28) that during the Early Carboniferous, the Alston and Askrigg Blocks were transgressed later than the flanking basinal areas. This pattern was the result of an Early Carboniferous eustatic sea-level rise, superimposed on which there was an epeirogenic sea-level change brought about by the differential subsidence rates of the basins and blocks.

Carboniferous blocks and basins

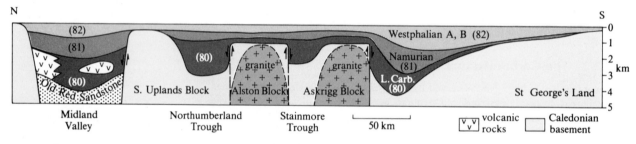

Figure 26 shows that the Alston and Askrigg Blocks are bounded by faults; some of these faults can be seen on both the Ten Mile Maps and the Lake District geological map. These faults were active *during* Early Carboniferous sedimentation, but as can be seen on Figure 26, only the fault along the southern margin of the Askrigg Block exerted a significant control on the thickness of Upper Carboniferous sediments.

Figure 26 Basins and Blocks in the Carboniferous. North–south sketch section from the Midland Valley of Scotland to St George's Land showing the thickness variations in Carboniferous strata above Caledonian basement.

As already mentioned in Section 6.4, on the basis of geophysical surveys, granite intrusions were postulated to form the cores of Alston and Askrigg Blocks. It was thought that these granites might be Variscan in age, providing the source of the abundant mineralization that can be seen in the Carboniferous of the north Pennines. Later, the presence of the granites was indeed confirmed by drilling, but the age was found to be Caledonian, comparable in age to the granites of the Lake District and Southern Uplands. These granites are now thought to form part of a large connected mass beneath northern England (see Lake District map, cross-sections 1 and 2). So clearly the intrusive episode was not the primary source for mineralization in the Pennines, although the higher *heat flows*[A] above them (due to the granites' higher conductivity) at later periods may have influenced the site of the mineralization.

The area of former Old Red Sandstone sedimentation in the Welsh borderlands was emergent during Lower Carboniferous times, and as stated earlier is generally known as St George's Land. It persisted in some form as an important palaeogeographic element for the remainder of the Palaeozoic and Mesozoic; as it continues eastwards into north France and Belgium, it is sometimes termed the *Wales–London–Brabant Massif*. It is in part a remnant of the Caledonian Midland Craton, (see Figure 13, Section 6.1) and is partly underlain by pre-Caledonian Basement.

Wales–London–Brabant Massif

* The Ten Mile Map (S) implies that the term Lower Carboniferous is used only in southwest England; this is not the case.

7.2.4 Carboniferous deltas

You may have noticed that some of the Lower Carboniferous successions illustrated in Figure 25 contain a repetition of a sequence of three rock types.

> Look at Figure 25 again, and determine the nature of this repetition and at which localities it occurs.

There is an upward repetition of limestone–shale–sandstone (you could have listed it starting with shale or sandstone, but you will see the reason for choosing to put the limestone first in a moment). These repetitive sequences dominate Carboniferous sequences in the Northumberland Trough and occur at the top of the Lower Carboniferous (spanning 'time slice' 6 of Figure 25) over the Alston and Askrigg Blocks, and in the Stainmore Trough. Sequences exhibiting this characteristic repetition are referred to as the Yoredale* Series. The *Yoredales* are a good example of cyclic deposition, and each cycle or repetition of rock types is termed a *cyclothem*.

Figure 27 is a lithological log summarizing the principal features of a Yoredale cyclothem. A typical cyclothem begins with a limestone containing abundant *crinoids*[A], *corals*[A] and brachiopods, finishes with a soil containing roots overlying which is a thin coal seam. The sediments between the limestone and coal consist of siliciclastics, beginning with shale above the limestone, but then *coarsening upwards* to cross-bedded sandstones.

> From Block 4, can you recall in what kind of environment this sequence would have been deposited?

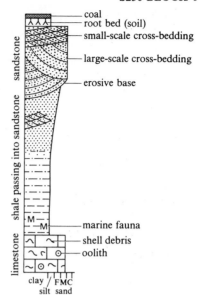

Figure 27 Idealized lithological log of a typical Yoredale cyclothem. The sequences may range in thickness between 5 and 20 metres.

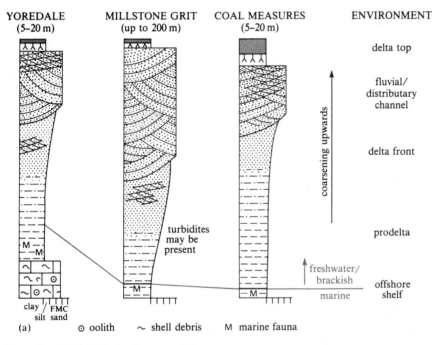

Figure 28 Idealized Carboniferous cyclothems:
(a) Simplified logs to show variations in the lithological successions of cyclothems of Yoredale, Millstone Grit and Coal Measures type. See Figure 27 for explanation of logs.
(b) Palaeogeographic sketch to show southward advance of Carboniferous delta systems in which cyclothems were deposited.
1, Scottish deltaic and fluvial system, active throughout Lower Carboniferous; 2, Lower Carboniferous delta of Northumberland; 3, Yoredale delta; 4, Millstone Grit delta.

The coarsening upward character, and the change from marine conditions up into non-marine sands topped by a soil and coal, suggests deposition by a prograding *delta*[A].

Cyclic deposition in the Carboniferous is not confined to the Yoredale Series, it is also common in the Millstone Grit and Coal Measures. The three types of Carboniferous cyclothem are summarized in Figure 28. Although they differ in thickness

---

* Named after Yoredale or Uredale, which are old names for what is now Wensleydale in North Yorkshire.

and the proportions of rock types present (there are no limestones in Millstone Grit and Coal Measures cyclothems), they all display a coarsening upward sequence capped by soils and sometimes coal. Thus they were all produced by delta progradation, which in the case of some Coal Measures cyclothems took place by delta growth into a lake rather than a shallow sea. Figure 28 also shows how the deltas responsible for the cyclothem sequences migrated southwards with time.

The cyclothems are interpreted as having resulted from a gradual *relative fall* in sea-level, as the base of the first two cyclothem types and many of the third were deposited in open marine (shelf) conditions, but the top is at or just above sea-level. Thus the *repetition* of cyclothems indicates *repeated relative changes of sea-level*. Each sea-level rise—or subsidence of the land—would push back the delta and flood the coal swamp deposits so that they would be overlain by limestone or shale. In time, deltas would advance into the area once more to produce another cyclothem. Of course, repetition of the cycles not only implies repeated changes of *relative* sea-level, but also *continued subsidence* in order that a succession of cyclothems may be preserved.

Many authors have suggested that the repetition of the Carboniferous deltaic cyclothems was due to epeirogenic causes, that is local earth movements changing relative sea-levels. Such movements would be extra 'pulses', additional to the continued subsidence described in the previous paragraph. Epeirogenic sea-level changes offer a satisfactory explanation for the origin of cyclothems that can only be traced over a relatively local area, such as the Yoredale Series in northern England. But because some 'marine bands' in the Coal Measures can not only be correlated across Britain but also into mainland Europe, it has been suggested that the Carboniferous cyclothems may have had a eustatic origin, especially as the southern super-continent of *Gondwanaland* is known to have been glaciated at this time. However, only a few marine bands are so extensive, and so many workers prefer to invoke an epeirogenic control.

Gondwanaland

A third hypothesis has been advanced to account for the cyclothems. This involves the rapid switching of the sites of deltaic deposition, a feature observed in modern delta areas. As a delta built outwards, a typical coarsening upward cyclothem would develop, but if the site of deltaic progradation suddenly switched to a new location, perhaps due to the river bursting its banks during a storm, continued subsidence would submerge the old delta top, and so result in marine sediments overlying, say, coal. At present, many geologists are happy to accept that all three hypotheses (eustatic and epeirogenic sea-level changes and delta switching) are valid to varying degrees.

7.2.5 Carboniferous palaeogeography

Now that we have dealt with the dominant themes of the Carboniferous history of the British Isles, namely the Early Carboniferous sea-level rise (transgression), sedimentation over blocks and basins, and cyclic sedimentation produced by the advance and retreat of deltas, it only remains to give an outline of *Carboniferous palaeogeography*.

Carboniferous palaeogeography

Figure 29 is a palaeogeographic sketch map of the British Isles at the end of the Early Carboniferous. The nature of the Yoredale series has already been described; it is confined to the Alston and Askrigg Blocks and the Stainmore and Northumberland Troughs. To the north, in the Midland Valley of Scotland, and also in the north and west of Ireland, occurs a mixed fluvial and lake environment, the latter sometimes containing evaporitic and organic-rich sediments.

The palaeogeography of the Early Carboniferous in most of the rest of England and Ireland is dominated by a shallow shelf on which limestones accumulated. The limestones are predominantly formed from *cemented*[A] 'skeletal sands' (composed of crinoids and brachiopods, and *ooid*[A] sands formed in shallow, warm, agitated waters broadly comparable to the environment of the present-day Bahama Banks described in Block 4—remember Britain was then on the Equator (Figure 3c and Colour Plate 6.4). Reef build-ups of carbonate sediment, bound together by a variety of organisms, often occur near the boundaries between relatively deep-water (basinal) and shallow-water (shelf) carbonate environments. The location of the reefs is comparable to that of many ancient and modern reefs, which often flank basin areas, as in the example of the Permian Capitan reef illustrated in TV 15 and discussed in Block 5, Section 7.3.4.

The area of basin sediments shown on Figure 29 accumulated dark grey shale and fine-grained *micritic*[A] limestones, which are often *bioturbated*[A]. These deposits

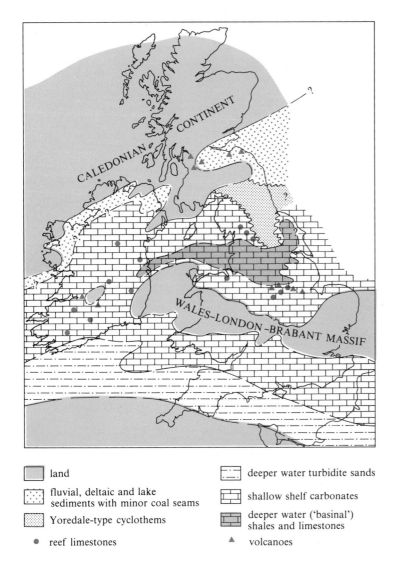

land

fluvial, deltaic and lake
sediments with minor coal seams

Yoredale-type cyclothems

● reef limestones

deeper water turbidite sands

shallow shelf carbonates

deeper water ('basinal')
shales and limestones

▲ volcanoes

Figure 29 Palaeogeographic sketch map for
the end of the Lower Carboniferous.

formed in low energy, rather deeper water conditions. Boreholes to the north of
Leicester have revealed the presence of evaporites beneath the basin sediments.
These evaporitic sediments probably formed as the Carboniferous sea began to
transgress the area.

Volcanic rocks are important in the Lower Carboniferous of the Midland Valley
and Northumberland; they are dominantly basaltic lavas.

In the south-west of Britain, relatively deep-water muds, some cherts, and turbidi-
tic limestones derived from the carbonate shelf were deposited in the Culm
Trough, and will be discussed again in the next Section, which deals with the
Variscan Orogenic Belt.

At the beginning of the Late Carboniferous, during the Namurian (81 on Ten Mile
Map), fluvial and deltaic systems advanced, both from the old Caledonian terrains
in Scotland, and to a lesser extent from the northern and southern flanks of the
Wales–London–Brabant Massif. In the Pennine Basin, the characteristic grit-
stones of the Millstone Grit (which are coarse-grained sandstones showing large-
scale cross-bedding) were deposited in fluvial channels that fed delta systems
fronted by turbidite fans (these were discussed in detail in Block 4, Section 7.7.2).
This deltaic advance is shown on Figure 28 (b), Section 7.2.4.

During the later part of the Late Carboniferous (Westphalian and Stephanian 82–
4), Coal Measures sediments were laid down, the economically productive part of
the sequence being largely confined to the Westphalian A and B (shown as 82 on
the Ten Mile Map) and the base of C. The distribution of coalfields (exposed and
concealed) in the British Isles and adjacent areas of Europe is shown in Figure 30.
Coal Measures of Stephanian age (Stephanian follows the Westphalian) tend to
contain more red sediments (84, Barren Red lithology on the Ten Mile Map (S))
indicating slightly more arid conditions, in contrast to the waterlogged swamps
typical of Coal Measures environments. The environmental interpretation of Coal

43

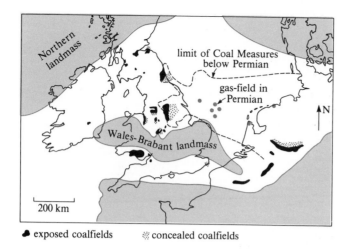

exposed coalfields   ※ concealed coalfields

Figure 30 Map showing the limits of Westphalian deposition and the occurrence of visible and concealed coalfields, and major gas-fields.

Measures cyclothemic sequences was discussed earlier (see Figure 28). The widespread extent, in time and space, of the typical Coal Measures delta-top 'swamp' environment is probably due to a fine balance between subsidence rate and the input of sediments from the Caledonian landmass and the Wales–London–Brabant Massif. This balance was such that only occasionally was the sea able to transgress the area to form the marine bands mentioned in Section 7.2.4, and sediments never built up sufficiently above sea-level for the local water-table to become dry enough to prevent swamp development.

Coalfields south of the Wales–London–Brabant Massif were affected by the Variscan orogeny. The coals were subjected to elevated temperatures caused by relatively higher heat flows and so lost most of their gas and other volatile components to become anthracite. However, to the north of the Massif, these volatiles were not expelled until after the Variscan orogeny, when the Coal Measures were buried deep beneath the thick Younger Cover of the North Sea. Some of these gases were trapped in the Younger Cover to form the major natural gas-fields shown on Figure 30.

7.3 The Variscan Orogenic Belt

7.3.1 Introduction

So far, in this Section, we have dealt with the rocks of the Older Cover that escaped the severe deformational effects of the Variscan orogeny. As you saw when examining the Ten Mile Map at the beginning of this Section, the British part of the *Variscan Orogenic Belt* is confined to the south-west of England, the Mendips, and the southernmost part of south Wales. It can be traced westwards into southern Ireland, and on the other side of the Atlantic from New Brunswick southwards along the Atlantic coast of the USA (see Figure 2b). Eastwards, the Variscan Orogenic Belt can be traced into northern France, Belgium and Germany and southwards into Spain and Portugal. It is in these countries that the most detailed studies have been made. Thus interpretations of the British part of the Belt rely heavily on studies made in mainland Europe.

Variscan Orogenic Belt

From the discussion of plate tectonics at the beginning of this Block, and that concerning the Caledonian orogeny (Section 6), it would seem reasonable to assume that the Variscan orogeny resulted from the closing of an ocean followed by continental collision.

What evidence is there on the maps you have studied to support such a view?

The large granites in south-west England could either have been formed above a subduction zone or be collision related. Certainly the more intense folding of Upper Palaeozoic strata suggests continental collision, and the *asymmetry*[A] of the folding (as observed on the Cheddar sheet) indicates northward directed movement, presumably *away from a* collision zone to the south. A detailed discussion of the geology of other parts of the Variscan Orogenic Belt is not possible here, but two general points are worth making.

There are sequences of basalts, gabbros and serpentinites (*hydrated*[A] peridotite) in the Variscan Orogenic Belt in mainland Europe, which have been interpreted as fragments of oceanic crust. The basic igneous rocks exposed around the Lizard Point in Cornwall are the only British example, thrust over Devonian rocks into their present location.

The distribution of fossil faunas suggests that by Late Silurian times, a wide ocean, termed the *Rheic Ocean*, separated southern Britain, northern France and Germany from Brittany and central Germany. Thus, it is likely, as shown in Figure 31, that Caledonian subduction events resulting from the closure of Iapetus were at least partly the result of the opening of the Rheic Ocean. In other words, the birth of one ocean resulted in the demise of another.

Rheic Ocean

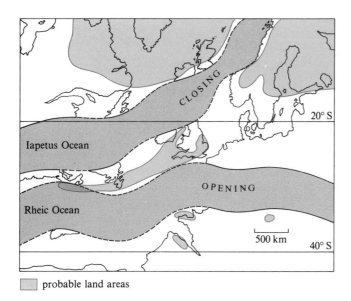

probable land areas

Figure 31 Reconstruction, based largely on fossil faunal evidence, of the Iapetus and Rheic Oceans in the Late Silurian.

The reconstruction presented in Figure 31 suggests that south-west England was situated on the northern margin of the Rheic Ocean during Late Silurian. As we shall see later, by Permian times almost the entire area depicted on Figure 31 was transformed into desert or was part of the vast super-continent of Pangaea (see Figure 3d, Section 2).

We now consider the extent to which the rock record in south-west England is consistent with these conclusions.

7.3.2 The rock record in south-west England

The structural complexity of the region, including the presence of numerous thrusts in south Devon and Cornwall makes it very difficult to relate sedimentary sequences together spatially to produce a regional palaeogeographic picture. However, a number of key features are worth describing.

In north Devon, there occurs a sequence of alternating continental fluvial sediments (Old Red Sandstone) and shallow marine siliciclastics. In south Devon, limestones, including reefs, occur, with some limestone turbidites representing slope deposits in front of the reefs. In Cornwall, a sequence dominated by slate contains volcanic *breccias*[A] and pillow lavas. The important point to note is that all the sequences are consistent with the hypothesis that during the Devonian the south-west of England was situated on a subsiding continental shelf and slope. The same seems to hold for Carboniferous successions. The Lower Carboniferous in Devon shows sediments similar to the Devonian basinal deposits, with the addition of cherts, which indicate low sedimentation rates and therefore probably relatively deeper conditions compared with the typical shelf limestones of the Carboniferous of the Older Cover to the north. The Upper Carboniferous consists of thick (perhaps up to 2 km) deltaic and turbiditic sediments, which are once again consistent with a shelf/slope location. The low sedimentation rates of the Early Carboniferous may be the result of a transgression pushing back the delta systems, thus reducing the influx of coarser siliciclastics.

The Devonian sediments occurring south-west of St Austell (SX(20)0152) in Cornwall are significantly different from those described above. They consist largely of turbiditic greywackes and conglomerates, containing mostly angular clasts of a variety of igneous, metamorphic and sedimentary rocks. Some volcanics are also present. These sediments are quite distinct from any others in south-west England. For this reason, it has been suggested that the sequence may have been thrust into its present location, and that the sediment may have been derived from a source area situated to the south.

The basic rocks around the Lizard Point (SW(10)7012) have already been mentioned. Although, on the Ten Mile Map, the associated metamorphic rocks are labelled as Precambrian, the rocks of the Lizard Complex have yielded radiometric dates mostly ranging between 371 and 350 Ma, but with several older dates, back as far as 492 Ma. The main cluster of dates probably represents a metamorphic episode in the events producing the Complex, and it has been suggested that older dates may indicate Precambrian Basement that has suffered a certain amount of argon loss (which would result in an age apparently younger than Precambrian—see Appendix). The ultrabasic nature of the Lizard Complex has led to the suggestion that it is a thrust slice of oceanic crust. The radiometric dates it has yielded are open to the interpretation that it is either Variscan ocean crust or a fragment of *pre*-Variscan ocean crust. What is not in doubt is that the Complex was emplaced in its present situation in the Late Devonian.

> Using the outcrop evidence on the Ten Mile Map (S), what can you say about the age of the granite intrusions in south-west England?

They cut across boundaries within the Upper Carboniferous, but their relationship with the Younger Cover cannot be seen. Therefore, we can, on map evidence alone, only state they are post-Late Carboniferous in age.

Geophysical evidence suggests that the series of granite outcrops is the surface expression of one continuous mass. Radiometric dates from these intrusions give an age of 270–280 Ma (Early Permian) and so clearly post-date the deformation of the Upper Palaeozoic sediments. Thus, the final deformation episode in south-west England can be dated as post-Westphalian (as it affects sediments of this age) and pre-Permian (i.e. pre-dating the age of the granites).

7.4 Synthesis

On the basis of data presented in earlier Sections, we can now turn to a consideration of the evolution of the crust beneath the British Isles during the Late Palaeozoic. Figure 2(b) shows the extent of the Variscan Orogenic Belt when continents bordering the Atlantic Ocean are shown in their pre-drift positions. As with the Caledonian orogeny, the distribution of the Variscan orogeny certainly favours closing the 'Atlantic' part of the Rheic Ocean between North Africa and North America, but for the Variscan of north-west Europe, the situation is much more complex. In Europe, the structures and outcrop trends show a series of arcuate (curved) patterns that are much more complex than the relatively linear trends we saw in the Caledonian Orogenic Belt. Although the Lizard Complex may be a thrust slice of Rheic oceanic crust, and the granites of south-west England may be collision or subduction related, there are three notable absentee plate tectonic indicators that were discussed at some length in the context of the Caledonian orogeny.

> Can you think what these absentees are?

There are no andesitic volcanics; there is no sign of the development of an accretionary prism; and there is no paired metamorphic belt in Britain (although such a feature does occur in the Variscan of mainland Europe). These differences between the Caledonian and Variscan Orogenic Belts (the complex structure of the Variscan and its lack of definitive subduction-related features) have led a number of workers to suggest that the Variscan orogeny is at least partly due to major transcurrent fault movements. This is very different from the postulated model for the Caledonian orogeny, which assumes almost head-on movement to close Iapetus. It is possible that the Variscan destructive plate boundary or boundaries involved both oblique subduction and lateral motion (*tear faulting*[A]). Past continental reconstructions favour considerable *dextral*[A] motion along the Rheic Ocean, as examination of the change in position of Britain relative to South America between Figures 3(b), (c) and (d) (Section 2) will show. Well over a dozen plate tectonic models have been proposed for the European Variscan Orogenic

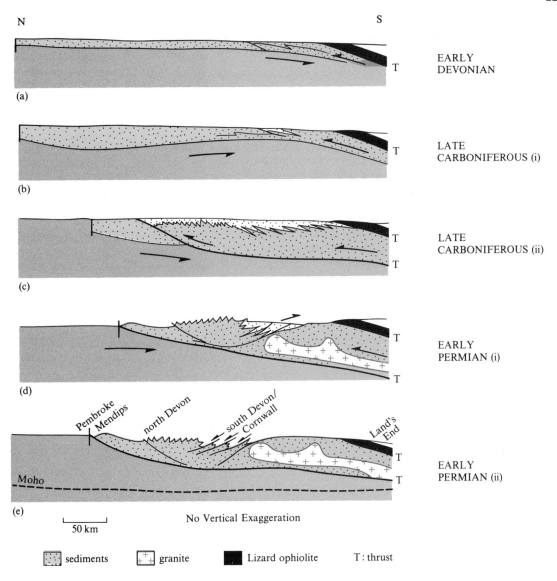

N   S

(a)   EARLY
       DEVONIAN

(b)   LATE
       CARBONIFEROUS (i)

(c)   LATE
       CARBONIFEROUS (ii)

(d)   EARLY
       PERMIAN (i)

(e)   EARLY
       PERMIAN (ii)

50 km   No Vertical Exaggeration

::: sediments   +| granite   ■ Lizard ophiolite   T : thrust

Figure 32 Possible model for the evolution of the Variscan Orogenic Belt in south-west England. Note how thrusting along décollement zones is contemporaneous with sedimentation during the Devonian and early part of the Late Carboniferous. The locations of Pembroke/Mendips, north Devon, south Devon/Cornwall and Land's End are shown on the bottom section. On sections (c)–(e), the boundary between the Variscan Belt and Older Cover is shown as a thrust. The presence of latest Carboniferous sediments shown on (c) is hypothetical; these sediments are shown being moved southwards by subsidiary thrusts in (d) and have been entirely removed by thrusting and erosion prior to the tensional movements shown in south Devon and Cornwall in (e). (To keep a vertical alignment of the various geological features of the Variscan Orogenic Belt in this Figure, we have shown the northern edge of the sediments apparently moving south. The sediments, granites, etc. are, of course, thrusting north over the Older Cover.)

Belt; here we will consider one possible model for the Variscan development of south-west England.

Figure 32 shows a model in which the Variscan Belt of south-west England, the Mendips and south Wales has been thrust northward along a décollement structure. This proposal is consistent with the tectonic structure of adjoining parts of the region, which has been shown with *seismic*[A] techniques to be a southward dipping décollement structure in the Variscan Belt in Germany. On the basis of geophysical evidence, the crust in south-west England is considered to be too thin (< 30 km) to have produced granitic magmas by melting continental crust beneath their present locations*. As subduction-related granitic magma generation also seems unlikely (there are no andesites in south-west England), it is envisaged that

---

* Adding some 5 km of crust eroded since the Permian still does not produce a thick enough crust.

the granitic magmas were generated at a destructive margin to the south of Britain, and injected northwards to produce a relatively thin sheet of granite with an irregular upper surface.

The Older Cover was not left unscathed by Variscan movements, and many of the tectonic structures within it bear the imprint of the underlying trend. This is because Caledonian structures were reactivated by Variscan movements. Examples of some structures affecting Upper Palaeozoic rocks with a Caledonian NE–SW trend are some folds in south-west Wales, and the Midland Valley rift in Scotland. Indeed, in the latter area, it is difficult to define when Caledonian movements ceased and Variscan ones began, because the rift continued to subside throughout the Late Palaeozoic. Likewise, the occurrence of andesitic volcanics in Scotland and Northumberland may reflect the continuation of the final effects of Caledonian subduction in the early Devonian. A new style of tectonism occurred at the beginning of the Carboniferous. This was essentially a rift phase (see Figure 8, Section 4.2), with blocks remaining high, but later in the Period, subsidence became more general with the maximum sag occurring between the Pennine blocks and St George's Land (see Figure 26, Section 7.2.3). We examined a manifestation of this rift-to-sag pattern in the Dalradian of Scotland, although in that case it may have been directly related to ocean opening to the south. In the case of the Carboniferous of northern England, rifting followed by subsidence probably occurred because of crustal thinning that never progressed far enough for the birth of a new ocean to occur.

The differential movement that caused the basin and block tectonic control of sedimentation probably followed Caledonian structures, particularly the granites that formed cores to the Lake District and the Alston and Askrigg Blocks. The main Variscan deformation phase at the end of the Carboniferous had a limited effect northwards of south-west England, south Wales and the Mendips. Folding in the Carboniferous of northern England is confined largely to areas between the blocks, and probably resulted from the vertical and lateral movements as the blocks were 'jostled' by Variscan events.

As with the Caledonian orogeny, crustal thickening led to uplift, and the development of a post-orogenic molasse-type deposit ensued, forming the base of the Younger Cover.

8 Younger Cover

8.1 Introduction

The development of the *Younger Cover* records the final phase of the plate tectonic development of the British Isles. Britain's geological history during the past 280 Ma has been affected by events at plate margins, both to the west as the Atlantic opened, and to the south as the Alpine orogeny progressed. During this period, the British area was not affected by ocean opening and closing events on the scale we examined earlier in this Block. This means that there is neither any uncertainty about the former width of vanished oceans, or the amount of crustal compression affecting the region during orogenies. Following the Variscan orogeny, the British Isles and the adjacent continental shelf areas drifted northwards to their present position as part of a single tectonic plate, the European plate, starting just north of the equator (see Figure 3d). This northward migration markedly changed the climate of the region (see for example Colour Plates 6.4 and 6.5). Likewise the opening of the Atlantic produced a significant climatic effect, with the Gulf Stream keeping north-west Europe significantly warmer than other locations situated at similar latitudes (e.g. Newfoundland, Labrador).

The changing palaeogeographies recorded in the rocks of the Younger Cover were produced by the superimposition of such climatic effects, global changes of sea-level, igneous activity and tectonic movements. In this Section, these aspects of the Younger Cover are examined in turn, before a brief review of the palaeogeographic evolution of the British Isles during the past 280 million years.

Younger Cover

8.2 Changing sea-levels

> Examine Figures 3 and 4, Section 2, and describe the global state of sea-level and distribution of continental crust 280 Ma to 220 Ma ago during the Permian and Triassic Periods.

During the Permian and Triassic periods, when the New Red Sandstone (85, 88–90 on the Ten Mile Maps) in Britain was being deposited, global sea-level was low, and the continents were assembled into the vast super-continent of Pangaea. These two facts are connected.

> Can you think why?

The suturing of the continents into Pangaea brought to an end a cycle of ocean opening and closure, so that there were probably relatively few active ocean ridges during the Permian. This meant that the total volume of ocean ridges was small compared to what it had been in the early Palaeozoic, or what it would be in the late Mesozoic. Thus relatively little water was displaced onto the continental shelves. Moreover, the glaciation of the southern continents during the Carboniferous and Permian would have also contributed to the late Palaeozoic sea-level fall.

From the beginning of the Jurassic onwards, global sea-level began to rise. The rise at the end of the Cretaceous resulted from the development of an entirely new system of ocean ridges, following the breakup of Pangaea (see Figure 3f). Not surprisingly, such a large rise had a significant effect on the types of sedimentary rocks that formed the Younger Cover.

> What kind of change of environment would you expect such a sea-level rise to produce?

The rise in sea-levels caused the replacement of *continental* desert conditions and land-locked evaporating seas characteristic of the British New Red Sandstone by the deposits of *warm shallow shelf seas* (e.g. the Jurassic and later rocks of Britain).

The global sea-level curve shown in Figure 4 is too 'coarse' to show fluctuations within a general rising or falling trend. We now know that the Mesozoic sea-level rise took place in a number of pulses. During periods of sea-level rises, shallow shelf, coastal and continental sedimentary environments were displaced landward and replaced by lower energy deposits.

> Applying *Walthers law*[A] and your knowledge of sedimentary processes and environments gained in Block 4, what kind of sedimentary succession would this produce? Would clays be replaced by shallow-water siliciclastics and limestones, or vice versa?

Shallow-water siliciclastic sands and limestones would be replaced by clays. With this lithological change in mind, part of the Mesozoic succession shown in the Ten Mile Map can be related in a general way to sea-level changes. The Lias (91-93) was deposited during a period of rising sea-level; this trend was interrupted by some falls that caused lithological changes that are too small to be shown on the Ten Mile map.

> Can you recall the dominant rock type of the Middle Jurassic in central England from the Moreton-in-Marsh geological map?

The Middle Jurassic was a period during which a fall in sea-level occurred (too short-lived to show up on Figure 4). Thus in southern Britain, shallow-water limestones dominate the sequence (94–95 on the Ten Mile Map (S) Inferior and Great Oolites). However, this fall was accentuated in the British area by tectonic uplift in the North Sea region, which caused the Middle Jurassic shallow marine limestones to be replaced northwards (in Lincolnshire, Yorkshire, the North Sea and Scotland) by deltaic and lake sediments.

In the Upper Jurassic, significant sea-level rises are recorded by the development of the Oxford Clay (97) and the Kimmeridge Clay (98). Early Cretaceous tectonic movements overshadow the effect of global sea-level changes in Britain at this time, but the Late Cretaceous rise (see Figure 4) can be detected on outcrop patterns on the Ten Mile Map.

ITQ 29 Describe the relationship between the Upper Cretaceous (105, 106) and older Mesozoic sediments (a) between Lincoln (SK(43)9872) and 15 km north of Market Weighton (SE(44)8842) and (b) along the Dorset and Devon coast at Swanage (SZ(40)0378) at Seaton (SY(30)2490) 70 km to the west, and north of Newton Abbott (SX(20)8771) 40 km further west.

In answering ITQ 29, you examined evidence for the presence of a major unconformity beneath the Upper Greensand or the Chalk in Yorkshire, Dorset and Devon. If you look on the Ten Mile Map at the base of outcrops of these Upper Cretaceous units, you will find more evidence for an unconformable relationship with older strata. In Northern Ireland, the Chalk (106), which forms a thin band beneath the Tertiary basalt (57) is shown on the Ten Mile Map as resting on Permo-Trias, Devonian and even Dalradian (18, 19, 27) (for example, just south of Fair Head in north-east Northern Ireland). This important regional unconformity is in large part due to the Late Cretaceous global rise of sea-level, but is also caused, as we shall see later, by significant earth movements of Early Cretaceous age. This *Late Cretaceous sea-level high* is the culmination of a general transgressive trend during the Jurassic and Cretaceous.

Late Cretaceous sea-level high

8.3 Igneous activity

Look at the keys to the Ten Mile Maps.

What is the age of the igneous activity shown that affects the Younger Cover?

The keys show extrusive igneous rocks of Permian (56) and Tertiary (North sheet only, 57–59) age.

The Permian extrusives are overlain by Permian sediments in the Southern Uplands (e.g. at NX(25)89), the Midland Valley of Scotland (e.g. at NS(26)42), and in south-west England (SS(21)90). But what about intrusive igneous rocks?

Look at the Ten Mile Map (N) between Tynemouth (NZ(45)3769) and Bishop Auckland (NZ(45)2030): there are outcrops of 35. What are they, and what is their age?

They are basaltic dykes (as shown by their straight-line outcrop pattern) and they intrude 82–3 (Westphalian) and *not* 86 (Magnesian Limestone). Therefore they must be pre-Magnesian Limestone–post Westphalian in age.

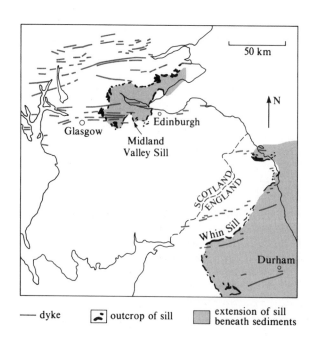

dyke ▭ outcrop of sill ▭ extension of sill beneath sediments

Figure 33 Late Upper Carboniferous sills and dykes of northern England and the Midland Valley of Scotland.

There are also more irregularly shaped outcrops of 35 in Northumberland that roughly follow the boundary between sedimentary formations 80 and 81.

> From TV 6 and Summer School, can you recall the name and type of this intrusion?

It is the Whin Sill.

A sill of similar age (but do not assume all outcrops of 35 elsewhere are the same age) occurs in the Midland Valley of Scotland (see Figure 33). The sills shown on Figure 33 have yielded radiometric dates of c.295 Ma, which is a Late Carboniferous age. Thus the igneous activity described above spans the Permian–Carboniferous boundary, and it seems that this *Permo-Carboniferous igneous activity*, which includes dyke intrusions (see Figure 33) and lavas, accompanied the final faulting phase of the Variscan orogeny which produced the fault-bounded Younger Cover basins that will be discussed in Section 8.4

Permo-Carboniferous igneous activity

Beneath the North Sea, there are a variety of locations and ages of igneous rocks, as shown in Figure 34. The early Permian volcanics in the North Sea area are, like their counterparts shown on the Ten Mile Map and Figure 33, a continuation of the igneous activity related to the final faulting episode at the end of the Variscan orogeny.

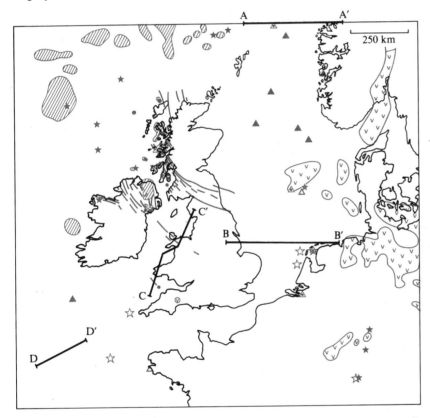

PERMIAN

ⓥ Early Permian lavas and pyroclastics

MESOZOIC

△ Triassic volcanics

▲ Middle Jurassic volcanics

⟁ Late Jurassic volcanics

☆ Late Early Cretaceous volcanics

★ Late Cretaceous volcanics

TERTIARY

• plutonic centres

— dykes

▨ lava fields

Figure 34 Location and ages of igneous rocks in the Younger Cover of the British Isles and adjacent shelf areas. Lines AA′, BB′, CC′ and DD′ are the locations of the structural sections shown in Figure 36.

Following the Permo-Carboniferous igneous activity, there were about 100 Ma lacking in igneous activity. Renewed activity began in the northern North Sea with the extrusion of Middle Jurassic lavas, but later volcanism in the Late Jurassic and Early Cretaceous (see Figure 34) was confined to the southern North Sea and during the Early Cretaceous to south-west of Land's End at Wolf Rock (SW(10)2512), incorrectly labelled as 46 on the Ten Mile Map). These periods of activity are related to important tectonic episodes that will be described in the next Section.

In north-west Britain, Tertiary igneous activity is widespread. Figure 34 shows the distribution of Tertiary igneous rocks in the U.K.; they may be divided into the three groups of igneous rocks, as described in Block 3, Section 3. These are: first, volcanic rocks, which are largely basaltic lavas and are well-developed in northern Skye, Mull and northern Ireland (Block 3, Section 4); second, minor intrusions, which include sills, *cone sheets*[A] and *ring dykes*[A], although the most conspicious minor intrusions shown on Figure 34 are dykes that radiate away from the igneous centres called *radial dykes*[A], which were described in Block 3 (Section 5); and third

Tertiary igneous activity

plutonic intrusions, which are largely composed of gabbro with smaller amounts of granite (see Block 3, Section 6).

The Tertiary igneous activity did not occur at a plate boundary. The opening of the Atlantic between Greenland and Europe at about 60 Ma was preceded by regional tension and rifting which set the scene for Tertiary igneous activity. This activity was along a (present) north–south line which was at an angle to the line of ocean opening, but broadly contemporaneous with it. The Tertiary igneous activity was very short lived, and most of the igneous centres shown on Figure 34 probably developed within a few million years of 60 Ma.

The relationships between lavas, dykes and plutonic complexes are poorly understood. In general, the lavas appear to pre-date the dykes and plutonic complexes. The lavas formed extensive *basaltic volcanoes*[A] (e.g. Northern Ireland; 4 000 km²) and *shield volcanoes*[A] centred, for example, on Skye and Mull. Within the framework, the central complexes consist of plutonic intrusions that formed deep beneath an ancient central volcano, sometimes referred to as the 'basal wrecks of large volcanoes'. They have therefore provided much information about the internal structure of volcanoes. Most intrusions, like that at Ardnamurchan described in TV 7, are arcuate in plan and grouped around one or a small number of distinct foci or centres.

8.4 Tectonic development of the Younger Cover

8.4.1 New Red Sandstone fault-bounded basins

As Figure 6, Section 3.2, shows, the distribution of Younger Cover shown on the Ten Mile Map is deceptive, for there is an extremely thick sequence in the North Sea, in the southern Irish Sea (Celtic Sea), and in the Western Approaches. So why is it that very little Younger Cover outcrops on land in the west and northern portions of the British Isles, north of a line running approximately between Newcastle and Exeter? You will begin to answer this question by completing the following ITQs.

> **ITQ 30** Look at the Lake District map, which, unlike the Ten Mile Map shows outcrop data for areas under the sea.
>
> (a) What stratigraphic unit forms most of the sea-bottom outcrop in the Irish Sea?
>
> (b) Look at the south-west end of geological cross-section number 2. What is the nature of the contact between the Younger Cover and older strata? Is it unconformable, or faulted, or both?

> **ITQ 31** Now look at the Ten Mile Map (S) sheet. Look along the coastline of Cardigan Bay from Tywyn (SH(23)5900) to Harlech SH(23)5830). Are the rocks abutting against the sea always Palaeozoic in age?

The answers to ITQ 30 and 31 show that in places the Younger Cover is faulted against older rocks, and downthrown seawards. In the case of the coast of Cardigan Bay, geophysical and borehole evidence shows Oligocene (110) to be faulted against Lower Palaeozoic rocks and underlain by a thick sequence of Lower Jurassic and Triassic rocks, as shown in Figure 35. Indeed, it is probable that Cardigan Bay is an example of an *exhumed topography*[A], which was initially developed in Permian and Triassic times, and then accentuated by later faulting. Many other smaller basins of Younger Cover are comparable. For example the oval-shaped Permo-Trias (89 and 90) Cheshire Basin to the south-west of Manchester shows faulted contacts with the Palaeozoic along much of its northern and eastern sides.

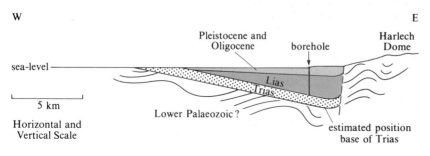

Figure 35 Sketch geological cross-section based on geophysical and borehole data, showing the faulted contact between Younger Cover and Caledonian basement (Lower Palaeozoic) in Cardigan Bay.

ITQ 32 Look at the Lake District map again, but this time at the onshore part. Can you find any faulted margins to Younger Cover basins here? Look for evidence on the map in the north-east corner and on the sections.

You have now examined evidence showing the oldest (New Red Sandstone) part of the Younger Cover occurs in *fault-bounded basins* in at least some parts of western Britain. In fact, some of these basins (and in particular the Vale of Eden) experienced active faulting during New Red Sandstone sedimentation. This pattern of fault-bounded basins extends up most of the west coast of mainland Britain from Cardigan Bay to the Western Isles of Scotland.

New Red Sandstone fault-bounded basins

8.4.2 Mesozoic tectonics

Figure 6, Section 3.2, shows that the Younger Cover is cut by *normal faults*[A] in the offshore basins around Britain. Knowledge of these offshore areas around Britain is relatively recent, having been acquired since petroleum exploration began in the

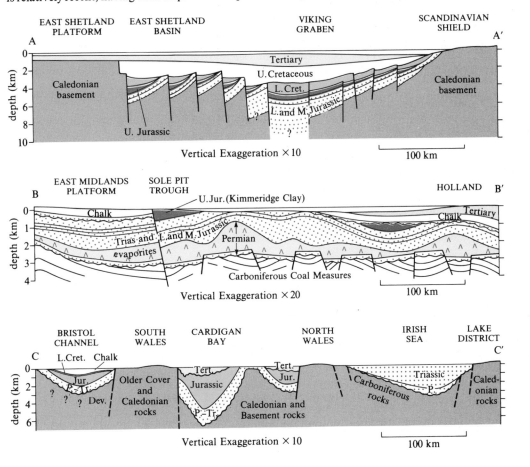

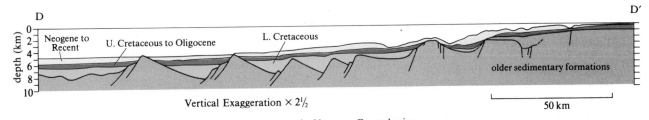

Figure 36 Sketch geological sections illustrating the structure in Younger Cover basins around the British Isles. The location of these sections is shown on Figure 34 (Section 8.3). Note that in sections AA′ and DD′ the Mid-Cretaceous age of faulting is clearly seen, for these structures do not extend into the Upper Cretaceous sediments. Some of these fault structures form important traps for oil in the North Sea. Section CC′ shows that in broad terms, present day topographic lows (the Bristol Channel, Cardigan Bay and the Irish Sea between north Wales and the Lake District) are the sites of fault-bounded basins. Permian evaporite sediments in places have flowed under pressure and have intruded younger strata, deforming them to produce anticlines. Natural gas that was generated from the coals was trapped in the Permian sands to form important gas-fields, which were 'sealed' by the overlying evaporite layer. (In Section CC′, the sea in parts of the Bristol Channel and Cardigan Bay is too shallow to show.)

North Sea in the early 1960s. Movement along some of these faults exerted an important control on the type and thickness of Jurassic and Cretaceous sedimentary sequences deposited. Quite dramatic thickness changes occur in fault blocks of the northern North Sea, because the blocks were tilted during sedimentation.

Faulting of comparable age can be detected in southern England by careful scrutiny of the Ten Mile Map. Look carefully at the map inland of the Dorset coast to the east of Lyme Regis at Burton Bradstock (SY(30)4889). To the north of Burton Bradstock is an outcrop of light yellow 95, and then partly overlapping with the word Bridport is a strip of 97, the northern margin of which is almost a straight line that, followed westwards, crosses over about 8 km outcrops of 95, 93, and 92, *but it abuts 105 to the east and does not continue through it*. This line is a fault (though not drawn as such on the Ten Mile Map), and as it does not affect 105 *it must pre-date it*. Around offshore Britain, there is plenty of evidence of faulting and uplift of comparable age (Figure 36). The unconformity at the base of the later Lower Cretaceous and Upper Cretaceous (105, 106) and the way the base steps westwards onto older and older strata (see ITQ 29 (b)) are clear indications of important tectonism that must have uplifted the south-west of England towards the end of the Early Cretaceous. *Mid-Cretaceous faulting* of similar age occurs throughout the northern North Sea and off the western margin of the British continental shelf at the end of the Western Approaches (see Figure 36, section DD'). The regional significance of this faulting will be discussed later.

Mid-Cretaceous faulting

You have already examined the unconformity beneath the Chalk in the Market Weighton area when answering ITQ 29 (a). This area also contains evidence of the effect of earth movements during the deposition of Jurassic strata.

> On the Ten Mile Map (S) sheet, look at the outcrop pattern of Jurassic between Lincoln (SK(43)9872) and Market Weighton (SE(44)8842) some 60 km to the north. What happens to the outcrop width of formations 91–97, and how can this change be accounted for?

The outcrop widths of formation 91–97 became narrower northwards to Market Weighton. The evidence available on the Ten Mile Map is not such that it is possible to determine whether the narrowing is due to an increase in the easterly dip of the strata nearer to Market Weighton, or whether it is because they thin to the north. Field measurements show the latter explanation to be correct, and this indicates that the Market Weighton area must have subsided less rapidly than the area to the south. This pattern of thickening and thinning of strata due to relative differences in subsidence rates is common in the Mesozoic of the British Isles, and the relatively 'low' and 'high' areas are respectively termed *basins and swells*. The effect of these on the thicknesses of Jurassic strata is summarized in Figure 37. It is probable that the relative movements causing the basins and swells result from the reactivation of fault structures in the Variscan or Caledonian basement.

basins and swells

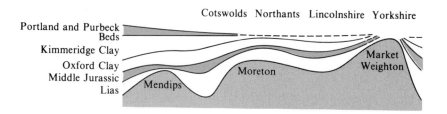

Figure 37 Sketch cross-section showing changes in sediment thickness of Jurassic strata between Dorset and Yorkshire. The strata are thickest in the basins and thin over the swells.

8.4.3 'Alpine' folding and faulting

'Alpine' folding and faulting

In Block 1 of the Course, and earlier in this Block, you examined evidence on the Ten Mile Map (S) for the presence of east–west trending asymmetrical (steeper northern limbs) folds in the Younger Cover of south-east England, and in the previous Section (8.4.2) in this Block, evidence for significant Mid-Cretaceous earth movements and faulting was outlined. Before the acceptance of the plate tectonic concept in geology, this deformation was considered to be a kind of 'ripple' effect, radiating out from the Alpine orogeny in southern Europe. However, these structures are now considered to be related to tectonic movements in the basement beneath the Younger Cover. We can explore the origin of these

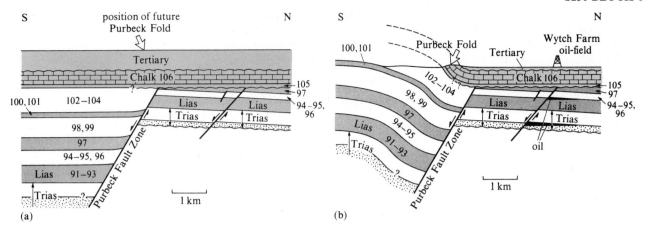

Figure 38 Structure of the Purbeck Fold.
(a) Structure before the Mid-Cretaceous movements that produced the Purbeck Fold. Note that some units are thinner on the north side of the fault (particularly 94–95, 96), indicating that movement along the Purbeck fault zone must have begun during the Jurassic, and perhaps even earlier. Note also that the major normal displacement along the fault pre-dates the Upper Greensand (105). (b) Present day structure, based on outcrop, borehole and seismic data. TV 2 demonstrated aspects of units 99–106, and the surface expression (outcrop pattern and relief) of the western end of the Purbeck Fold.

structures by studying an example you first examined at the beginning of Block 1: the Purbeck fold on the Dorset coast. As Figure 38 shows, the evidence for *normal* faulting in the region is quite clear; it was post-Lower Greensand (104), pre-Upper Greensand (105) in age.

> There are thickness variations in certain sedimentary units across the fault zone. What is the cause of this thickness variation across the fault?

It is probable that some movement also occurred during sedimentation in the Jurassic and possibly even earlier. During the Jurassic and early Cretaceous, this fault probably behaved as a listric fault—that is, it was curved, flattening out at depth. It has been calculated that these listric fault movements were caused by about 2.5 km of crustal extension in the basement rocks beneath the area.

The Purbeck fold is itself evidence for *reversed* movements during the Tertiary (probably Miocene) and was the result of approximately 1.5 km of crustal *shortening*. These extensional and compressional movements probably occurred along major structural weaknesses in the Variscan basement, which were then transmitted up through the Younger Cover. The east–west trend of the Purbeck fold and similar folds in southern England such as the Chalk Hogs Back to the west of Guildford (TQ(51)0050) are certainly consistent with the hypothesis that the underlying control was exerted by movement in the Variscan basement, which at outcrop also shows similar structural trends (e.g. in the Mendips).

The change in tectonic style from normal to reversed movements occurred between the Late Cretaceous and Cenozoic in many parts of north-west Europe and the North Sea. It may be as much related to the change from rifting to spreading along the future Atlantic margin to the west of Britain as it was to orogenic events in southern Europe.

8.5 Palaeogeography

8.5.1 Introduction

As stated earlier, palaeogeographic reconstructions of the British area for the past 280 Ma are not complicated by uncertain amounts of lateral movements caused by ocean closure and continental collision. Past geographies were influenced by ocean opening and the separation of once-united continents that now border the North Atlantic, but it is possible to plot these relatively precisely using palaeomagnetic and *sea-floor magnetic anomaly*[A] data. The discussion that follows is centred on a series of palaeogeographic sketch maps that will place in a historical context the influence of tectonism, igneous activity, changing sea-levels, and climate on the development of the Younger Cover.

It must be stressed that these maps are very generalized, for they attempt to summarize the distribution of the dominant features that characterize a given period of geological time. Thus they condense onto one map a considerable amount of variation that may have occurred through time intervals ranging from several to over twenty million years.

8.5.2 Permian and Triassic (New Red Sandstone)

Colour Plate 6.5 shows a reconstruction of the Vale of Eden area during the Permian, based on the succession of rocks exposed in the area. Many other parts of the British Isles and its adjacent continental shelf areas contain similar rocks. Figure 39 shows two successions from the North Sea area.

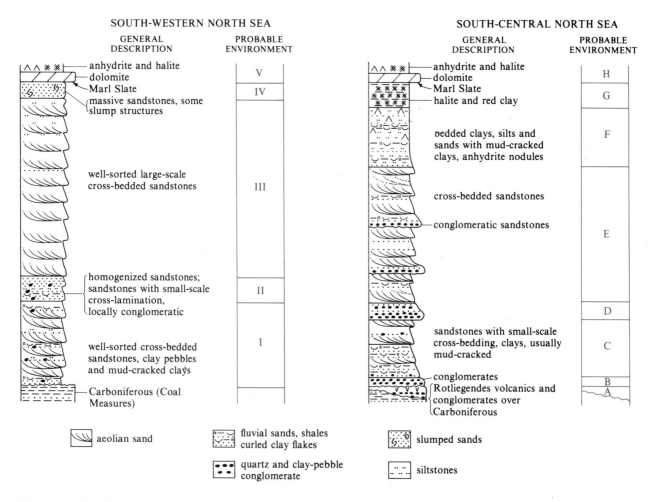

Figure 39 Lithological successions of Lower Permian age encountered in oil exploration wells in the North Sea. For use with ITQ 33.

ITQ 33 From your knowledge of desert environments gained in Block 4 (especially TV 11) interpret the numbered and lettered portions of the successions shown in Figure 39 by matching them against the following descriptions:

wadi[A]	marine evaporite
aeolian[A]	desert lake
mixed aeolian and wadi	marine reworking
inland sabkha	volcanic

The basal Permian usually rests with marked unconformity on older strata, and often exhibits considerable 'palaeorelief'. The Lower *Permian* consists of *desert* sediments, either a mixture of angular breccias and poorly sorted sand laid down in alluvial fans, or *dune*[A] sands which may occur in association with the fans, or as

Permian deserts

56

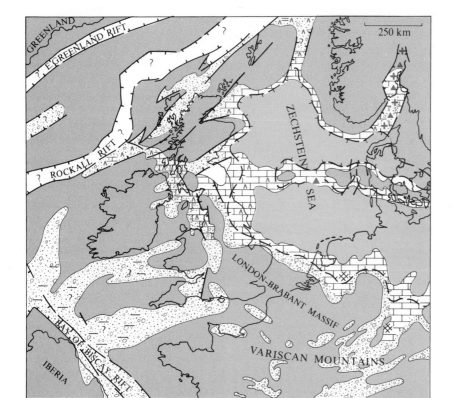

▨	land
▤	red shales
▨	continental sandstones and conglomerates
▥	carbonates (dolomites and limestones)
∧∧	anhydrites
▨	thick halites
Ⅽ⌐	maximum extent of halite
✳	evaporites within other sediments
▲	volcanics
+	intrusive igneous rocks
⌐⌐	active fault zones

Figure 40 Palaeogeographic sketch map for the Late Permian. The Zechstein Sea reached its maximum extent at this time, and was fringed by carbonate deposits of the Magnesian Limestone and Permian Marls (86, 87 on Ten Mile Map). Rift zones to the west of the British Isles were initiated during the Permian, and later became the sites of ocean opening (see Figure 48).

separate dune fields bordering the evaporitic Permian sea. The sands are important gas reservoirs in the North Sea, where the unit is generally known by its German name, the Rotliegende ('red layers'). During the Late Permian, dune sediments persisted in Scotland, but in the Midlands and south-west England, the Upper Permian may be absent, or represented by red marls. In north-east England, the Upper Permian at outcrop is represented by the Magnesian (i.e. dolomitic) Limestone and the Permian Marls from which original *Permian evaporites* have largely been dissolved away. But to the east, below the Cretaceous and Jurassic strata of the North Sea, thick sequences of evaporites occur, and these thicken considerably eastwards.

Permian evaporites

Thus, at this time, north-east England lay on the margin of an extensive inland sea (see Figure 40) subjected to high evaporation rates. It is now thought that this inland sea was successively filled (perhaps by water spilling over a shallow barrier) and evaporated to produce a series of evaporite cycles. This inland sea is generally known as the *Zechstein Sea*, after the German term used for the interval. The thick evaporites that formed in this sea played an important role in the southern North Sea in producing structures in which natural gas is trapped. The evaporite minerals, especially halite, are less dense than the surrounding sediments and deform very easily, and flow upwards under pressure to produce intrusive diapiric structures which deform the flanking rocks. In the southern North Sea, these *diapirs*[A] have created traps for natural gas, and the evaporites have also formed an effective impervious seal to Rotliegende reservoir rocks. Thus, the important gas-fields in the area owe their origin to the distribution of gas source rocks (coals) in the Carboniferous and the occurrence of overlying porous sandstone reservoir rocks sealed on top by evaporite minerals.

Zechstein Sea

The lower part of the Triassic is dominated by conglomerates and pebbly sandstones referred to as the Bunter Pebble Beds (named after the equivalent horizon in Germany), although modern workers recognize more local formational names. These sediments were laid down by braided rivers flowing largely northwards from Britanny and also to a lesser extent from the Wales–London–Brabant Massif. The Upper Triassic, apart from around small remnants of the Variscan mountains

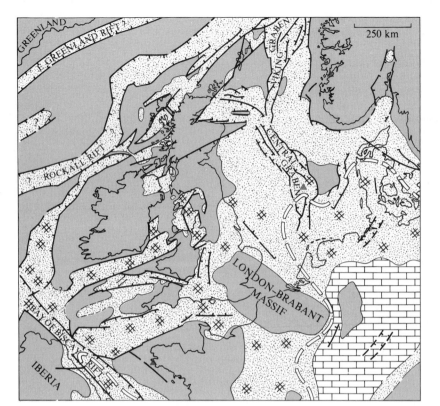

land

continental sandstones and shales

marine limestones of mid-Triassic age

maximum limit of marine limestones

evaporites (mainly halite)

volcanics

active fault zones

Figure 41 Palaeogeographic sketch map for the Triassic. During the Middle Triassic, a marine transgression resulted in the deposition of shelf limestones in central Europe. This sea never reached the British Isles area, where continental conditions prevailed, and evaporite deposits formed in extensive playa lakes, including thick halites in the Cheshire Basin, which today are mined to provide 'road salt'.

such as the Mendips, consists mostly of fine-grained marls containing anhydrite and *gypsum*[A]. These were probably laid down in ephemeral *playa lakas*[A], which sometimes precipitated halite, as in the Cheshire Basin and north-west England (see Figure 41).

8.5.3 Jurassic

During the early part of the Jurassic, the red unfossiliferous desert sediments of the New Red Sandstone were replaced by dark grey *ammonite*[A]-bearing shales and clays, with some low energy limestones. This change marks the beginning of the transgression that continued (albeit with some regressive interruptions) until nearly the end of the Cretaceous. At the beginning of the Early Jurassic, the remaining land areas (see Figure 42) were probably of low relief, for little coarse clastic material is present except for restricted fringes of coarse material around the land masses. Organic-rich shales occur in the southern part of Britain and in northern France and central Germany, and these provide a source for oil in these regions, but are not an important contributor to North Sea oil-fields.

During the Middle Jurassic, the central part of the North Sea was uplifted into a *dome*[A]. A rift system with three converging grabens became well developed in the northern North Sea area. This can be seen on Figure 43; it was associated with extensive basaltic volcanics. The dome-shaped uplift resulted in an influx of siliciclastic sediments into surrounding areas, thus accounting for the northward change at this time from limestone (as seen in the Moreton-in-Marsh area) to siliciclastics. The siliciclastic sands in the North Sea are important oil reservoirs.

During the Late Jurassic (Figure 44), continued movements occurred along faults, many of which were initiated during the domal uplift and its subsequent collapse. These movements were particularly important in the northern North Sea, where in places *fault scarps*[A] were developed, and from them were built submarine and alluvial fans, both of which are now important as oil reservoir units. In the Kimmeridge Clay (99), organic rich shales also occurred in deeper waters, and these (which are both equivalent to, and younger than, the Kimmeridge Clay of southern England) are considered to be the major source of North Sea oil.

58

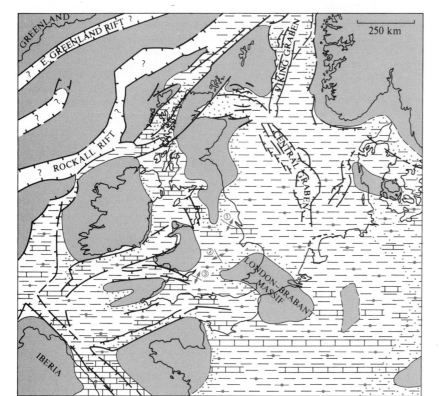

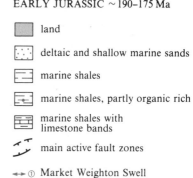

- land
- deltaic and shallow marine sands
- marine shales
- marine shales, partly organic rich
- marine shales with limestone bands
- main active fault zones
- ① Market Weighton Swell
- ② Moreton Swell
- ③ Mendip Swell

Figure 42 Palaeogeographic sketch map for the Early Jurassic. During this interval, the British Isles experienced a major transgression, and so Triassic deserts were replaced by extensive shelf seas. The land areas had by now been eroded down to a relatively low relief, and so little coarse siliciclastic sediment was deposited on the margins of the Early Jurassic sea. In relatively deep-water areas, bottom conditions became oxygen deficient, and so organic-rich shales were deposited. These are the source rocks for the oil in the Wytch Farm Oil-field of Dorset, in which one of the reservoirs is a Lower Jurassic sand (see Figure 38).

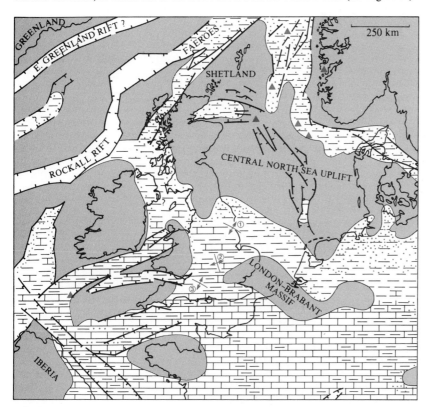

MIDDLE JURASSIC ~175–160 Ma

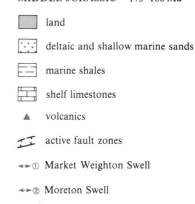

- land
- deltaic and shallow marine sands
- marine shales
- shelf limestones
- volcanics
- active fault zones
- ① Market Weighton Swell
- ② Moreton Swell
- ③ Mendip Swell

Figure 43 Palaeogeographic sketch map for the Middle Jurassic. This was dominantly a regressive episode, which in the British Isles area was caused both by a global fall in sea-level and the uplift of the central part of the present North Sea region. This uplift was the cause of the major facies change from deltaic sands in Yorkshire (which are similar to several oil reservoir sands in the North Sea) to shallow shelf limestones in the Cotswold area. Note the association of volcanic centres with the North Sea rifts.

59

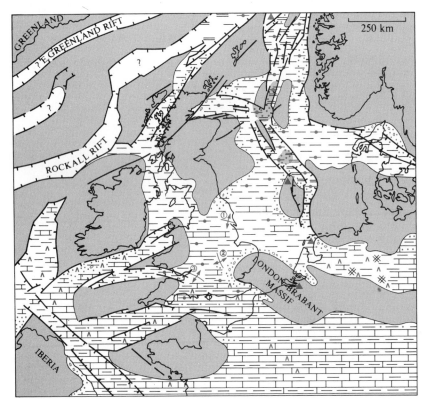

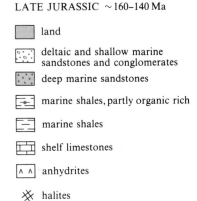

Figure 44 Palaeogeographic sketch map for the Late Jurassic. A global rise of sea-level caused the deepening of the shelf seas, and so organic rich shales (e.g. the Kimmeridge Clay, 99) accumulated once more, to become the major source rock for North Sea oil. Collapse of the Middle Jurassic central North Sea uplift and major movements on the North Sea rift system and other faults (such as the Great Glen Fault) resulted in the accumulation of thick turbiditic sands in fault-bounded basins. To the south and south-west in latest Jurassic time, evaporitic conditions characteristic of the Purbeck Beds (101) occurred.

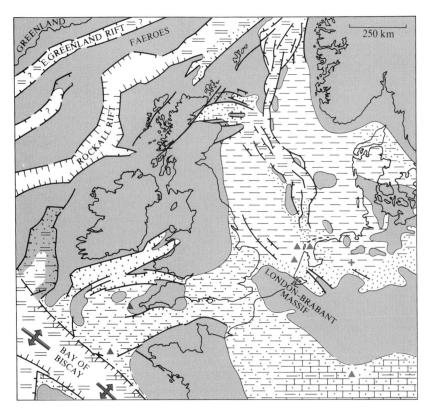

Figure 45 Palaeogeographic sketch map for the late Early Cretaceous (roughly equivalent to 104, Lower Greensand, on the Ten Mile Map). Overall, the distribution of land and sea areas is similar to that of the Late Jurassic, save that the land area in the south-east North Sea area had diminished in size. Shallow marine sands dominated in southern Britain, where they are underlain by continental (fluvial, lake) sands of the 'Wealden' Beds (102–103), which were replaced to the north by marine strata. To the south-west, the Bay of Biscay opened as Iberia parted company with mainland Europe.

As the British area had drifted northwards out of arid latitudes, no sediments characteristic of desert conditions are present in the Jurassic.

8.5.4 Cretaceous

In southern England, the topmost Upper Jurassic and lower part of the Lower Cretaceous were deposited in continental lagoonal, lake and fluvial conditions characteristic of the Purbeck Beds (101), Hastings Beds (102) and Weald Clay (103), whereas north of the Wales–London–Brabant Massif, the Cretaceous is entirely marine in character (and therefore shown collectively as 102–5 on the Ten Mile Map (S). The development of continental facies in southern England, which interrupts the general Jurassic–Cretaceous transgressive trend, was in part related to the Mid-Cretaceous earth movements described earlier. These caused the uplift of south-west England so that the Variscan granites were exposed and eroded, shedding siliciclastics eastwards. Figure 45 is a palaeogeographic sketch map for the later part of the Early Cretaceous.

During the Late Cretaceous, the palaeogeographic picture of the British area was drastically changed, as Figure 46 shows. There was an extensive relative rise in sea-level, flooding much of the former land masses, and those that remained were probably of low relief, as very little siliciclastic sediment is found in any sequence. In addition to the Late Cretaceous transgression (which is considered to have been caused by the growth of the volume of ocean ridges displacing oceanic waters), the tectonics of the region changed from the former fault-controlled block subsidence, to a general sag in the North Sea area where up to 1 km of Chalk sediments accumulated (Figure 36 AA′, Section 8.4.2). This change in tectonic style from rift to sag is reminiscent of that already discussed in the Carboniferous of northern England and the Dalradian of Scotland.

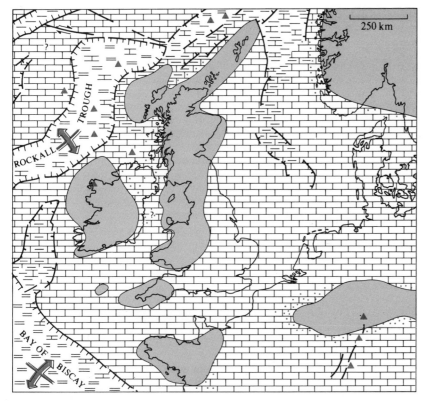

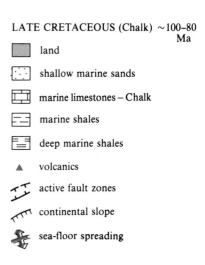

LATE CRETACEOUS (Chalk) ~100–80 Ma

- land
- shallow marine sands
- marine limestones – Chalk
- marine shales
- deep marine shales
- ▲ volcanics
- active fault zones
- continental slope
- sea-floor spreading

Figure 46 Palaeogeographic sketch map for the Late Cretaceous. The reduction in size of land areas reflects the major Late Cretaceous global sea-level rise, which may have been over 300 m higher than that of today. The virtual absence of siliciclastic sands indicates that land areas had extremely low relief and therefore supplied little sediment; indeed, some workers believe that the 'Chalk sea' may have entirely covered Scotland, Wales and Ireland. The Bay of Biscay was almost completely opened to its present width at this time, the Irish continental margin had separated from its Canadian counterpart (not shown), and the Rockall and Greenland Rift Zones (the latter now out of the frame of this map) had changed to ocean spreading axes (although some workers believe this change occurred during the Early Tertiary). Movement along fault zones was much diminished, with the predominant tectonic style being a regional 'sag' in the North Sea region, which permitted over 500 m of Chalk to accumulate there (see Figure 36 AA′).

8.5.5 Tertiary

ITQ 34 There are two widely separated areas on the Ten Mile Map sheets where rocks occur of vastly different type, but both of which are Tertiary in age. Where are these areas and what are the rock types?

In southern England, relatively thin Tertiary sedimentary sequences occur, which are onshore extensions of sequences that reach a total of 3 km thicknesss in the North Sea, and up to 2 km in the Western Approaches (see Figure 6, Section 3.2). Whereas sediments in the North Sea show little folding and some faulting, those of south-east England have been deformed by folding and some faulting of probable Neogene age that was discussed in Section 8.4.3. In north-west Britain, igneous activity was widespread (see Figure 34, Section 8.3) and consisted of extensive lava fields, dyke swarms and plutonic igneous rocks.

In the Hampshire and London Basins, the Tertiary sequences are a mixture of shallow marine and non-marine sands and clays. Their faunas and floras indicate that a subtropical climate prevailed. These structural basins were discrete depositional basins during the early Tertiary, being separated by the newly uplifted Weald. The marine influence increased to the east in the London Basin, and to the south-east in the Hampshire Basin. Despite the general *regressive*[A] trend of sea-level during the Tertiary, rapid subsidence of the North Sea area resulted (see Fig. 36 AA', Section 8.4.2) with a largely marine sequence accumulating. Deltaic and submarine fan complexes built eastwards from the Shetland Platform area (for location, see Figure 47). These sediments were derived from the newly uplifted source lands to the west, the uplift being related to the development of the Tertiary igneous centres described earlier. The North Sea subsided or sagged as a large basin area in contrast to the predominantly rift-controlled basins of the Mesozoic.

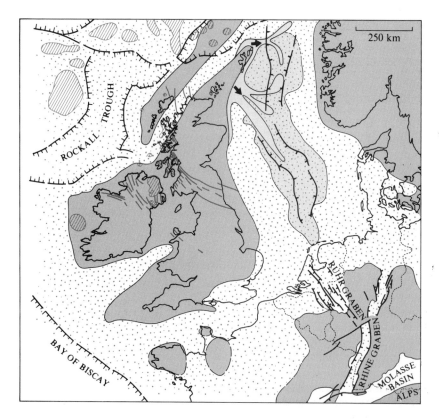

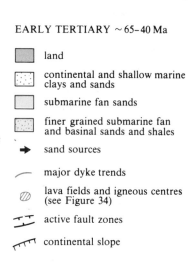

EARLY TERTIARY ~ 65–40 Ma

- land
- continental and shallow marine clays and sands
- submarine fan sands
- finer grained submarine fan and basinal sands and shales
- sand sources
- major dyke trends
- lava fields and igneous centres (see Figure 34)
- active fault zones
- continental slope

Figure 47 Palaeogeographic sketch map for the Early Tertiary. Two features dominate this interval in the north-west European shelf area. To the north-west was the Tertiary igneous province and its associated uplift. The latter resulted in siliciclastic sediments being shed eastwards to fill the major North Sea 'sag' which accumulated over 3 km of submarine fan sands, which form important reservoirs for both oil and gas. Far to the south, the Alps were already rising, shedding sediments northwards into the Molasse Basin, north of which the Rhine rift system or graben was developing.

8.6   Summary and conclusions

The preceding sections have summarized briefly the development of the Younger Cover in terms of past latitudinal (i.e. climatic) and sea-level changes, and a number of tectonic episodes. During the 280 Ma time span in which the Younger Cover developed:

The British Isles migrated from a low latitude position in which an arid climate prevailed, to its present-day high latitude position, which is ameliorated by the Gulf Stream to give a temperate climate.

Following the Late Palaeozoic when sea-level was low, the remaining history of the Younger Cover is dominated by a rising overall trend of global sea-level, which reached a maximum in the Late Cretaceous, after which sea-level fell.

Earth movements and igneous activity occurred at the end of the Carboniferous and in the Early Permian, and the movements produced fault-bounded basins. Uplift of the northern North Sea occurred during the Middle Jurassic and was associated with volcanism. During the Late Jurassic, important faulting occurred contemporaneously with sedimentation over most of Britain and its adjacent continental shelves. This movement continued into the Early Cretaceous, after which the 'rift' style of basin subsidence was replaced by an extensive regional subsidence or 'sag' in the North Sea.

To conclude this Section dealing with the Younger Cover, you should consider how the tectonic and igneous events described earlier relate to rifting and sea-floor spreading events in nearby regions.

> **ITQ 35**   Figure 48 is a sketch map showing the timing of continental separation and collision events adjacent to the British Isles. What relationship, if any, can you see between these events and the following episodes in the development of the Younger Cover:
>
> Middle Jurassic volcanism and uplift in the North Sea;
>
> Tertiary igneous activity;
>
> Mid-Cretaceous earth movements;
>
> Faulting and folding of the Younger Cover in southern England;
>
> Change from a rift to a sag subsidence pattern in the North Sea.

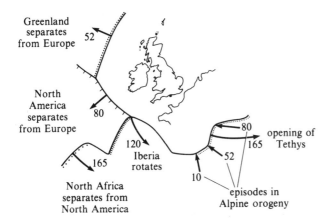

Figure 48   Sketch map showing the timing of continental separation and collision in regions adjacent to the British Isles. The numbers give the date in Ma before present, and the arrows the direction of movement.

In answering ITQ 35, you will have realized that a mid-plate region, such as the British area was during the development of the Younger Cover, is not totally immune from the effects of processes operating at plate margins.

9 The Quaternary Ice Age

9.1 Introduction

In geological terms, the Quaternary is a very short period, lasting so far* only
c. 2 Ma, whereas the Tertiary had a duration of c. 63 Ma and the Carboniferous
c. 65 Ma. Nevertheless, the Quaternary does stand out distinctly in the geological
record because it marks a period of considerable global climatic instability, quite
different from conditions during the Jurassic, Cretaceous or Tertiary. Evidence
both from fossil faunas and floras and from estimates of ocean water temperatures
suggest that during the Mesozoic and Tertiary, climates changed relatively slowly,
episodes of abrupt change being rare. On the other hand, the Quaternary has been
characterized by repeated cycles of rapid climatic change.

Continuous sedimentary records through the Tertiary and Quaternary only exist
on the floors of the deep seas and oceans and perhaps in a few very ancient African
lakes. Cores of ocean sediments, such as those recovered during *deep-sea drilling*[A],
frequently contain abundant assemblages of microfossils, particularly the tiny
calcareous skeletons of *planktonic*[A] Foraminifera. Many of the species concerned
can still be found living today, and from knowledge of their present-day ecology it
is possible to estimate the temperatures, or rather palaeotemperatures, of the
surface waters in which different fossil assemblages of these Foraminifera from
different depths in the cores were living. This kind of evidence shows that towards
the end of the Tertiary there developed on a global scale repeated cycles of
alternately warmer and cooler climate with a period of about 10^5 years; they are
known as *glacial–interglacial cycles*. These cycles became very much more pro-   **glacial–interglacial cycles**
nounced about two million years ago, and during the colder intervals, expansions
occurred of *glacier ice*[A] on land (see Colour Plate 6.6) and also of floating pack ice
on the oceans, especially in the Northern Hemisphere. Seventeen cycles occurred
during the last 1.8 Ma, and they affected not only temperate latitudes, but also
tropical and subtropical regions, where changes in temperature and especially
rainfall took place.

The Quaternary ice age is, however, not a unique event in geological history.

> During which other geological periods have you encountered evidence of ice
> ages?

Already, from this Block you know that tillites occur in Precambrian Dalradian
sequences in Scotland, dated to about 670 Ma. In fact, we know of at least four
separate ice age events at different times during the long span of the Precambrian
(see Table 1, Section 2). There is also evidence from North Africa for a further ice
age during the Ordovician, and during the Permo–Carboniferous in Gondwanaland. There is, however, at present no evidence at all for any ice age event during
the Mesozoic.

9.2 The onset of glacial conditions

Ice cover around the poles seems to develop when the polar areas become partly
isolated from the main paths of the Earth's atmospheric and oceanic circulation.
Thus the Antarctic is isolated by the circum-Antarctic wind and ocean current
systems. Ice cover was established there as long ago as the Oligocene, when these
current systems were established following the final separation from Antarctica of
Australia, and of South America, which had originally formed part of a single large
continental plate, Gondwanaland.

However, the kind of climatic pattern that we refer to as an ice age (which involves
an unstable climate and extension of ice sheets into temperate latitudes) was only
established much later, towards the end of the Tertiary, when plate movements

---

* It has not finished yet!

also led to the partial isolation of the Arctic Ocean. Important factors were probably:

The closure of the strait between North and South America, which initiated a totally new ocean current system in the Atlantic including the development of the Gulf Stream;

The shallowness of the Bering Strait between Asia and North America which limits (or cuts off entirely during sea-level lows of glacial periods) the flow of water from the Pacific into the Arctic Ocean.

The resulting deterioration of climate in the Northern Hemisphere is shown by the first development of glacial deposits in Iceland at about 3.5 Ma. Probably the first major continental glaciation of Europe took place at about 2.3 Ma, for palaeobotanical studies show that many temperate tree *genera*[A] became extinct at this time. It is uncertain when the highlands of Britain were first glaciated during the Quaternary, but this probably occurred over a million years before the first surviving tills were deposited in lowland Britain about 0.5 Ma ago. The size of glacial erosional land forms, such as *cirques*[A] and glacial troughs cut by *valley glaciers*[A] suggest that an enormous amount of glacial and *glacifluvial*[A] erosion and *mass movement*[A] under *periglacial climates*[A] must have taken place since the end of the Tertiary, thus implying long periods of ice cover.

9.3 Quaternary deposits and geological maps

So far this Block has relied heavily on geological maps to help trace the geological history of Britain. However, on the Ten Mile Map, the only Quaternary strata shown are the early Pleistocene* Crag deposits (115), a series of marine shelly sands and clays that represent an ancient transgression over the North Sea across East Anglia, prior to the main glaciations of Britain. Likewise, on your Lake District map, no Quaternary deposits are shown, although from reading Block 4 and perhaps from general knowledge you may have realized that this mountainous area suffered glaciation during the Quaternary.

Do any of your other geological maps show Quaternary deposits?

Yes, on Solid edition 1:50 000 or one inch to the mile maps, Quaternary deposits are not coloured, but are shown only by symbols, except where they are of limited extent. The pre-Quaternary strata are shown by colours and their boundaries have to be deduced where they are hidden by Quaternary deposits. Solid and Drift edition maps manage to combine both kinds of information on a single sheet, as on the Cheddar and Moreton-in-Marsh sheets.

ITQ 36 What kinds of deposits are referred to as drift on the geological maps in your collection?

Note in particular that the Moreton-in-Marsh sheet shows spreads of both boulder clay (till) and glacial gravels, so clearly the area was glaciated.

9.4 The glaciations of Britain

The Crag deposits of East Anglia (115 on the Ten Mile Map) are of Early Pleistocene age and are older than any glacial deposits known in Britain. Nevertheless, they are often very fossiliferous, and studies of *molluscs*[A] and Foraminifera suggest that faunas now more characteristic of Arctic waters were alternating with warm water faunas in the North Sea, so already the typical Quaternary pattern of climatic change had been established.

Although the most spectacular evidence for glaciation in Britain comes from mountain areas, the history of repeated glaciation can best be worked out in the lowlands. Extensive areas of Britain are still covered by till and glacial gravel deposits (Figure 49a). The distribution of these deposits gives a rough impression

---

* The Quaternary is traditionally subdivided into Pleistocene and Holocene (or Recent) subdivisions. The latter represents only the last 10 000 years of post-glacial time and is increasingly regarded by geologists as representing merely the latest interglacial period of the Pleistocene.

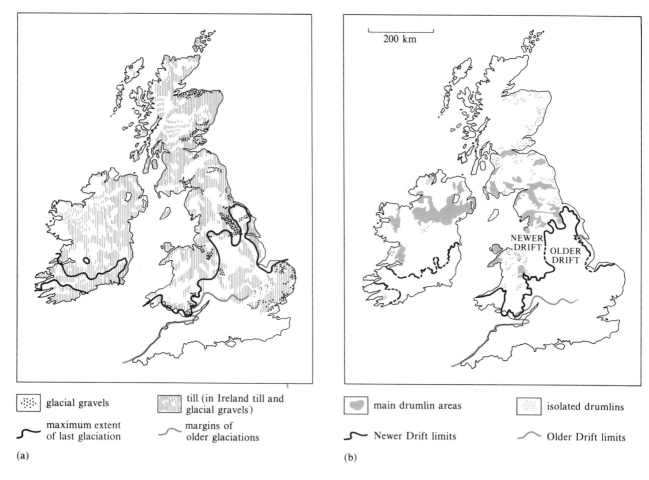

:::: glacial gravels	till (in Ireland till and glacial gravels)
⌐ maximum extent of last glaciation	margins of older glaciations

(a)

main drumlin areas	isolated drumlins
⌐ Newer Drift limits	Older Drift limits

(b)

of the maximum area of ice cover in Britain during the Quaternary. Considerable erosion and removal of till deposits has occurred locally; also not all areas were glaciated during the same ice advances.

At least three major, and several minor, ice advances have taken place in lowland Britain during the last 0.5 Ma. The oldest of these penetrated deep into southern East Anglia, reaching the Chilterns, north London and the edge of the present Thames Valley (Figure 49a). It was this advance that diverted the Thames (as described in TV 12) from an older course that ran across East Anglia to join the sea on the Essex Coast, possibly near Clacton. A later ice advance involved a thick ice sheet spreading down the Irish Sea Basin, impinging on the Devon and Cornish coasts, and even reaching the Scilly Isles. The latest glacial stage of the Quaternary lasted from about 80 000 to 10 000 years ago, but the main period of actual ice advance took place only 25 000–15 000 years ago. As you can see from Figure 49(b), the extent of this glaciation in Britain was less than during the previous major glacial episodes, for ice barely reached the Midlands or East Anglia.

We shall not discuss here the stratigraphic evidence for these ice advances, but you should note that they were separated not only by short interglacial episodes of temperate climate and vegetation, lasting ten to twenty thousand years, but also by even longer unglaciated, but nevertheless intensely cold periods during which periglacial processes were very active. The deep-sea sedimentary record demonstrates clearly that, for most of the Quaternary, climatic conditions have been much colder than they are today, not only in Britain, but in virtually all the present temperate areas of the world.

The study of land forms, particularly land forms of glacial deposition such as drumlins[A], kettleholes[A] and hummocky moraine[A], is extremely important in our understanding of the recent Quaternary history of Britain. Often these land forms can be used to reconstruct quite detailed local patterns of ice advance and retreat, since, unlike erosional land forms, they relate to particular stages in the Quaternary and even to particular local geological events.

Examine the distribution of drumlins in the British Isles shown in Figure 49(b). How does this relate to the overall distribution of glacial sediments shown in Figures 49(a) and (b)?

Figure 49 The distribution of glacial deposits and the limits of ice advances in the British Isles.
(a) Distribution of tills and glacial gravels.
(b) The limits of Older and Newer Drift.

Drumlins only occur within the margins of the last major ice advance. They certainly belong to that glaciation, because when a glacier invades an area it tends to destroy and rework the unconsolidated deposits over which it passes, such as the tills of older glaciations. This ice advance has left behind a landscape characterized by fresh depositional features—not only drumlins but also moraines, *eskers*[A], *kames*[A] and kettleholes. Their distribution makes it possible to map fairly accurately the maximum limits of the last big ice advance. Deposits left by the most recent extensive ice advance are known as the Newer Drift.

Newer Drift

You can see from Figure 49 that to the south and east of the margin of the last glaciation extends an area glaciated by the two older ice advances and still possessing widespread patches of till and glacifluvial deposits. However, although these deposits have not been reworked by ice, river downcutting and mass movement have destroyed virtually all the glacial land forms. If you look at the distribution of glacial deposits on the Moreton-in-Marsh sheet, you can see how they have only survived on flat-topped hills and plateaux. The deposits beneath such features are referred to as the *Older Drift* and have been subject not only to glaciation but to a long period of subsequent periglacial activity thoughout the last glacial period.

Older Drift

The latest episode in the glacial history of Britain took place relatively recently. The main ice sheet of the last glaciation melted very rapidly, and by 13 000 years ago summer temperatures at least were as warm as at the present day. Suddenly, however, the climate deteriorated again, and it is a measure of how erratic and how rapid Quaternary climatic changes can be, that during a very short interval (c. 11 000–10 500 years ago) known as the *Loch Lomond Readvance* a large ice cap was re-established in the western highlands of Scotland, as were *cirque glaciers*[A] in the mountains of Wales and the Lake District. By 10 000 years ago, these glaciers had melted as rapidly as they had appeared. In the Scottish highlands, and elsewhere at high altitude, they left behind the freshest and best preserved hummocky glacial landscapes, moraines and glacifluvial deposits to be found anywhere in Britain. They also left a reminder that climatic change on this scale could certainly be repeated.

Loch Lomond Readvance

9.5 Beyond the glaciations

In Section 8 of Block 4, we stressed that the Quaternary ice age and its glaciations had much wider effects than on the landscape actually affected by ice. Both *permafrost*[A] and a wide variety of periglacial processes affected not just southern England, but most of the rest of Britain. During long cold periods, the amount of water locked up in ice caps grew so that the sea-level fell, resulting in Britain being joined to the continental mainland of Europe. The vegetation was dominantly of a tundra type, consisting of bog and open ground with a discontinuous cover of Arctic herbs, grasses and dwarf shrubs. There was a mammal fauna of mammoth, reindeer, woolly rhino and muskox, or perhaps horse and bison when conditions became slightly milder. Only in the short interglacial periods did a warmer climate permit the growth, first of coniferous forest, such as is now found in Scandinavia, then of deciduous forest with oak, elm and ash, such as we have in Britain today. The interglacial fauna consisted not only of familiar animals such as deer, badger and fox, but also of exotic species, such as straight-tusked elephant, hippopotamus, lion and hyaena, which are now extinct or confined to tropical regions.

Humans also first appeared in Britain during the interglacial periods, and they eventually mastered the periglacial environment as hunters of mammoth, bison and reindeer. Stone tools are found in Quaternary lake sediments, in river gravels and rarely as *erratics*[A] in tills. Only in Post-glacial times did humans develop the skills of crop and animal husbandry that ultimately permitted the development of urban civilizations. These skills were first developed in the Near East, but reached Britain with the first Neolithic peoples about 5 500 years ago. With the development of modern civilizations, humans have largely imposed their own ecosystems on our landscapes, and their activites are now both changing those landscapes and modifying many of the geological processes that sculpture them.

Self assessment questions

SAQ 1 (*Objectives 2 and 3*)   Using the Table below, summarize the main features of the litho-tectonic units that comprise the rock record in the British Isles. (A few entries have already been made as a guide to the type of entry to make.)

	Stratigraphic age of rocks	Igneous activity		Metamorphic rocks (state type: slate, schist etc)	Structure	
		Intrusive (including age)	Extrusive		Major faults	Fold trends, asymmetry
Younger Cover			Tertiary plateau lavas in W. Scotland, Ireland			
Older Cover	Devonian and Carboniferous				Midland Valley boundary faults	
Variscan orogeny		SW England Permian granites		Regional type— produced slates		
Caledonian orogeny						
Precambrian Basement:						
NW Scotland				Lewisian, high grade		
elsewhere				Not discussed		

SAQ 2 (*Objective 4*)   Summarize under the following headings the evidence on which plate tectonic interpretations of the Caledonides are based:

(a) Evidence for the former existence of the Iapetus Ocean;

(b) Evidence for subduction;

(c) Evidence for continental collision.

SAQ 3 (*Objective 6*)   (a) Draw a simple lithological log of a Carboniferous cyclothem, indicating the environmental interpretation given to each part of the sequence, and (b) comment on how the sea-level changes indicated by the succession of environments might be caused.

SAQ 4 (*Objective 7*)   Give examples you have met during this Block of the tectonic control of patterns of sedimentation. You should be able to think of four, two of which are on a large plate tectonic scale, whereas the other two are more localized.

SAQ 5 (*Objective 8*)   Briefly outline how plate tectonics, eustatic sea-level and climatic change are interlinked, and give examples from this Block.

Objectives for this Block

When you have completed this Block, you should be able to:

1   Define, or illustrate using sketches, or recognize on geological maps as appropriate, the terms listed in Table A.

2   Summarize the principal features of the main litho-tectonic units of the British Isles, namely *Precambrian Basement, Caledonian Orogenic Belt, Variscan Orogenic Belt, Older Cover, Younger Cover.* (ITQs 1—20, SAQ 1)

3   Summarize the differences beween the Basement in north-west Scotland, England and Wales. (SAQ 1)

4   Summarize the evidence on which plate tectonic reconstruction of the evolution of the Caledonian Orogenic Belt are based. (ITQs 21–24, SAQ 2)

5   Be able to draw palaeogeographic sketch maps of the British Isles during the Devonian and Early Carboniferous (Not tested; see Figures 24 and 29 (Sections 7.2.1 and 7.2.5) for the kind of map you should be able to draw; these Periods are selected because of your Summer School studies).

6   Be able to sketch a graphic summary of an idealized Carboniferous cyclothem and summarize the three modes of origin proposed for them. (SAQ 3)

7   Describe British examples of the tectonic control of sedimentation, including accretionary prisms, block and basin sedimentation, basin and swell sedimentation, and rift to sag patterns of sedimentation. (SAQ 4)

8   *Briefly* (in a few sentences) summarize how plate tectonics, sea-level and climatic change are interlinked, giving examples from this Block. (SAQ 5)

Appendix   Radiometric dates—a cautionary note

Many Sections of this Block describe geological events in terms of their absolute age e.g. 500 Ma. Although a detailed discussion of radiometric dating techniques is beyond the scope of this Course, it is important that you realize that these dates may mean different things in different rocks. You should not assume that they are exactly comparable to historic dates, such as 1066, for they were not recorded by an observer using a calendar, but are based on the decay schemes of *radioactive elements*[A]. Thus the results depend not only on the limitations of the analytical method, but on the nature of the rocks or minerals investigated, and on their *entire* history (i.e. later events may blur earlier ones).

The principle of absolute dating of rocks is based on their content of radioactive isotopes as was explained in the Science Foundation Course.* The method is based on the decay schemes of a number of elements in which a *parent element*[A] decays to a *daughter element*[A].

The results may be obtained by concentrating certain minerals and then analysing them, or by analysing 'whole rock' samples. Radiometric dates give the age when parent and daughter isotopes became 'locked' in the appropriate minerals of a rock. For an igneous rock this means that the date obtained indicates a stage in the rock's cooling history. When certain minerals crystallize, isotopes become fixed, and daughter isotopes remained trapped as they formed. For metamorphic rocks, the 'event' dated is the crystallization and cooling of the minerals containing the parent and daughter isotopes. And for sedimentary rocks, the dates are usually obtained from the iron aluminosilicate mineral glauconite which forms just beneath the sediment–water interface by post-depositional processes. Thus the dates represent more or less the time at which the sediment was deposited. In all these cases, the date obtained is usually a minimum date, for magma intrusion precedes cooling, metamorphism acts on pre-existing rocks, and the sediment dates are based on diagenetic minerals that formed after deposition. In addition, if any loss of daughter isotopes occurs (which is more than likely in the case of argon, which is a gas), then this will reduce the age measured.

The dates quoted in this Block are usually the mean of clusters of dates obtained from a particular group of rocks. The use of such dates is essential in the Precambrian, for there is no biostratigraphic framework. In the Phanerozoic, we can refer to 'dates' using either rock names at the Series level (these are *lithostratigraphic*[A] units e.g. Old Red Sandstone) or time names (*chronostratigrapic*[A] units e.g. Devonian), as well as using the absolute calibration in millions of years of these units.

ITQ answers and comments

The answers to ITQs 1–20 describe the principal features of the litho-tectonic units of the British Isles.

Younger Cover

ITQ 1 *Stratigraphic age* range: Permian (85) to Pleistocene (115)

ITQ 2 *Nature of contact with older units*: unconformable.

ITQ 3 *Folding*: You studied examples of folds affecting the Younger Cover (Block 1, Section 2.3) on a local scale on the Dorset coast, and on a smaller scale when examining the outcrop patterns around the *synclines*[A] of the Hampshire and London basins, and the Wealden *anticline*[A]. You should recognize that these folds have general east–west axial plane trends, and are asymmetric, with the northern limbs of their anticlines *dipping*[A] more steeply.

ITQ 4 *Onshore and offshore thickness contrasts*: Figure 6 shows that the onshore parts of the Younger Cover (i.e. those depicted on the Ten Mile Maps) are relatively thin (mostly less than 1 km thick) in contrast to the very thick offshore parts, which are up to 6 km thick in the northern North Sea. These offshore *basins*[A] have been discovered during exploration programmes for oil and gas, and their origin will be discussed towards the end of this Block.

Older Cover

ITQ 5 *Stratigraphic age*: Devonian and Carboniferous (75–84)

ITQ 6 Significant outcrops of *volcanic rocks*, (53–55) occur in the Midland Valley of Scotland. You may have spotted small outcrops in the Derbyshire area, but these are relatively minor compared with the Scottish sequences.

ITQ 7 *Relationships with Caledonian Orogenic Belt*: (a) In most of Britain, the Older Cover overlies unconformably rocks of the Caledonian Orogenic Belt. In Block 1, you explored one example of this unconformity at Ingleton (see Block 1, Section 2.4). (b) However, the major exception to this relationship is on the flanks of the Midland Valley of Scotland, where the Older Cover is *faulted*[A] against older rocks. The relationship between the Older Cover and rocks of the Variscan Orogenic Belt will be explored in ITQ 12.

ITQ 8 *Nature of tectonic structures*: Like the Younger Cover, the Older Cover has only suffered relatively minor deformation in comparison with the orogenic regions. (a) The *Midland Valley* region, which is a *rift valley*[A] or *graben*[A], was produced by faulting of probable Late Carboniferous age that affected many other regions. The north margin of the rift is bounded by the *Highland Boundary*

---

* S101, Unit 26 *Geological Time*

Fault, and the south by the *Southern Uplands Fault*; both faults trend NE–SW. (b) Some folding also occurred, such as that which produced a north–south trending anticlinal structure in the Pennines area visible on the Ten Mile Map (S).

Variscan Orogenic Belt

ITQ 9 *Stratigraphic age of rocks involved*: Devonian and Carboniferous, with Precambrian metamorphic rocks (29, 30) present around the Lizard Point (SW(10)72) and Start Point (SX(20)8337) areas. These metamorphic rocks are *thrust*[A] over the folded Devonian strata, but the thrusts are not shown on the Ten Mile Map, so you could not be expected to make such an interpretation. If you were particularly observant, you may have spotted a tiny outcrop of 69 (Llandeilo, Ordovician) at SW(10)9139.

ITQ 10 *Intrusions*: You should have interpreted the large red (34) outcrops in south-west England shown on the Ten Mile Map as granite intrusions. From geophysical evidence, it is known that the granite extends beneath the surface connecting the present day outcrops.

ITQ 11 *Fold patterns*: You should have noticed from the Ten Mile Map that strata of Devonian age (76–78) outcrop along the north Devon coast, and again along the south Devon coast and in Cornwall. These two Devonian outcrop strips are separated by a broad belt of Carboniferous (80–83), preserved in the axial part of a synclinal structure. This fold structure is termed a complex syncline because a variety of scales of smaller folds can be seen in the field superimposed on the larger scale fold, but these cannot be detected on the Ten Mile Map. You may remember from your study in Block 1, Section 4.4.1, of the 1 : 25 000 Cheddar Sheet that in the Mendips, Carboniferous and Devonian strata are folded with the axial planes of the folds trending roughly east–west. The anticlines show steeper northern limbs. Thrusts are also present, and are shown on the Cheddar sheet. To the west (and somewhat to the north), on the Gower Peninsula east of Worms Head (SS(21)4087), and in the southernmost part of west Dyfed (Pembrokeshire) north of St Govans Head (SR(11)9793), tight folds can be seen on the Ten Mile Map. These trend WNW–ESE.

ITQ 12 *The northern limit of the Variscan Orogenic Belt*: although the boundary is shown as a distinct line on Figure 6, it is not possible to locate it precisely using the outcrop patterns visible on the Ten Mile Map. The Variscan terrain of south-west England shows relatively intensive folding in the form of an east–west trending complex syncline; this intense folding is not visible on the Ten Mile Map. In the Mendips, Gower and west Dyfed (Pembrokeshire), a series of less intense asymmetric folds occur, and can be seen on the Ten Mile Map. In the Mendips, the fold trends are east–west, but they are WNW–ESE in Wales. The more open syncline of the south Wales coalfield is clearly associated with this folding, but on Figure 6 is not included in the Variscan Orogenic Belt. To the north of Bristol (ST(31)57), fold axes are oriented north–south, and so are clearly different to the general east–west Variscan trend. Thus the *tectonic* distinction between Variscan and Older Cover terrains is not sharp but *gradational*.

ITQ 13 *Relationship to older rocks*: The only pre-Variscan rocks seen are associated with thrusts, except for a tiny *inlier*[A] of Ordovician at SW(10)9139. It is not possible to say anything further about what underlies rocks of the Variscan Orogenic Belt, although it is clear the belt has been thrust over Precambrian metamorphic rocks at SX(20)83 north of Start Point and over metamorphic and ultrabasic rocks at SW(10)72 north of Lizard Point.

Caledonian Orogenic Belt

ITQ 14 The Caledonian Orogenic Belt can be divided into two parts, the metamorphic and non-metamorphic parts. Caledonian terrains to the north of the Midland Valley of Scotland are metamorphic (Dalradian (13–25) and Moine (8–12)), and those to the south are non-metamorphic sedimentary formations.

ITQ 15 *Non-Metamorphic Caledonides*: Cambrian (64) to Silurian (74).

ITQ 16 *Fold structures*: in central and north Wales, the outcrop patterns indicate major folds with NE–SW trending axes. These are well displayed in the south-west corner of the 100 km square SJ(33). Here, south-west trending tongues of 70–72 occupy anticlines extending into younger 73–74. This fold trend can be followed towards west Dyfed (Pembrokeshire), where it swings to a more east–west trend. This NE–SW grain can also be seen in outcrops of 70–1, 72 and 73 in the non-metamorphic Caledonian terrains of the Southern Uplands of Scotland. It is generally referred to as the Caledonian structural trend. Note that the Midland Valley of Scotland, which is a graben or rift valley preserving Older Cover, follows this trend, suggesting some link between Caledonian and later events.

ITQ 17 *Relationship to underlying Basement*: In Anglesey, on the Lleyn Peninsula to the south-west and in a small area along the Menai Straits, the Ten Mile Map shows Lower Palaeozoic rocks resting unconformably on Precambrian rocks, including metamorphics.

ITQ 18 *Metamorphic Caledonides*: It is possible to discern a general NE–SW Caledonian trend, particularly in the outcrops of Dalradian (13–25). Likewise some major faults with this trend are marked on the Ten Mile Map (N), including the Great Glen Fault, which cuts south-west across the Highlands from Inverness (NH(28)64) on the Moray Firth along Loch Ness to Loch Linnhe. This fault is an important *transcurrent fault*[A], the movement of which may have begun during the Caledonian orogeny, and certainly continued into the Mesozoic.

ITQ 19 *Relationship of the Metamorphic Caledonides to the underlying Basement*: the Ten Mile Map (N) shows major thrusts separating the Metamorphic Caledonides from the underlying Basement. The latter consists largely of Precambrian metamorphic rocks of the Lewisian Complex (1–7), and Precambrian sediments (incorrectly labelled as Palaeozoic on the Ten Mile Map (N)) of the Torridonian (61), plus some Cambrian and Ordovician sediments (62, 63, 67). Thus the boundary between Metamorphic Caledonides and Basement is tectonic and is known as the Moine Thrust Zone. Some of the rocks of the Basement are unaffected by metamorphism, yet they are overlain, above the thrust, by the metamorphic rocks of the Moine.

ITQ 20 *Granitic intrusions in the Metamorphic and Non-Metamorphic Caledonides*: examination of the Ten Mile Map (N) shows that large granitic intrusions (34) occur in both types of Caledonian terrain, in Scotland and north England, but they do *not* occur in Wales.

ITQ 21 In general terms, the rocks become younger south-eastwards across the Southern Uplands, with a north-western strip of 70–1 (Ashgill and Caradoc), a central strip of 72 (Llandovery) and south-eastern strip of 73 (Wenlock). Detailed examination of the boundary between 70–1 and 72 reveals that it is quite complex, with numerous sharp kinks. In addition, there is an inlier of 70–1 north of the red granite outcrop at NX(25)57, plus a number of small diamond-shaped inliers. All these complexities are due to the sequence being folded. These diamond-shaped inliers and similarly shaped, but smaller outliers of 73 are the result of isoclinal folding: however, we did not expect you to interpret this from the Ten Mile Map.

ITQ 22 At its base, it shows a thin sequence of Ordovician cherts, *tuffs*[A], lavas and black shales, followed by about 5 km of Silurian *greywackes*[A].

ITQ 23 Thin cherts and black graptolitic shales indicate slow deposition in relatively deep water, whilst the great thickness of the greywackes suggests rapid deposition associated with an unstable slope triggering turbidity flows.

ITQ 24 The main differences between the Lake District and Southern Uplands may be summarized as follows:

	Lake District	Southern Uplands
Sedimentary sequences		
Silurian:	Mainly greywackes	Shales and greywackes, with some cherts and basaltic lavas at base of successions in faults blocks
Ordovician:	Thick andesitic volcanics with some basaltic and rhyolitic lavas, unconformably overlying mudstones and greywackes with some volcanics	
Igneous rocks	Thick series of andesitic volcanics (Borrowdale Volcanic Group)	Thin basaltic lavas
Structure	Relatively broad folds; absence of *reverse faulting*[A] and isoclinal folding	Tight folding and series of fault blocks inclined to north-west

ITQ 25 (a) The Lower Palaeozoic of the Welsh Basin is virtually complete, whereas there are significant gaps over the Irish Sea Platform (Cambrian and Upper Silurian missing) and the Midlands Platform (most of the Ordovician and the Lower Silurian missing).

(b) The Welsh Basin accumulated over 10 000 m of sediment and volcanics during the Early Palaeozoic, in contrast to the thinner incomplete successions over the Irish Sea Platform and Midland Platform.

(c) Turbidites are confined to the Welsh Basin, and Ordovician volcanics also only occur in this area and the adjoining slope, with minor amounts in the Silurian of the Midlands Platform, and none over the Irish Sea Platform.

ITQ 26 Table 4 is a completed version of Table 3. See main text for further discussion.

ITQ 27 You should have made descriptions of the nature of Variscan folding along the following lines:

(a) South-west Wales: WNW–ESE trending fold axes with steep dips (as shown by narrow outcrops widths); several tight anticlines and synclines;

(b) The Gower Peninsula shows folding similar to south-west Wales, but the slightly broader outcrop widths indicate less steep dips. The south Wales coalfield is a broad syncline, with its eastern closure indicating a basin-like structure. Steeper dips on the south-

Table 4 Completed version of Table 3 (ITQ 26)

	1 Moray Firth area	2 Midland Valley	3 SW Southern Uplands	4 Northumberland and NE S. Uplands	5 Lake District & Cross Fell	6 Ingleton	7 North Wales	8 Nuneaton	9 Moreton-in-Marsh	10 Dyfed (Pembrokeshire), south Wales coalfield	11 Mendips	12 SW England
(a) CARBONIFEROUS												
84 Westphalian & Stephanian:	—	—	—	—	√	√	√	√	√(2)	√	—	√(3)
82–3 Westphalian (mainly 'Coal Measures')	—	√	√	√	√	√	√	√	√(2)	√	—	√(3)
81 Namurian (Millstone Grit)	—	√	—	√	√	√	√	—	—	√	√(4)	√(3)
80 Tournaisian & Viséan (Carboniferous Limestone Series)	—	√	√	√	√	√	√	—	—	√	√	√(3)
(b) DEVONIAN/O.R.S.												
78 Upper Old Red Sandstone	√	√	√	√	—	—	—	—	—	√	√	√(1)
Devonian Limestone	—	—	—	—	—	—	—	—	—	—	—	√
75 Lower Old Red Sandstone	√	√	—	√	—	—	—	—	—	√	—	√(1)
(c) VOLCANIC ACTIVITY												
49–52 Devonian Volcanics	—	√	—	√	—	—	—	—	—	—	—	√
53–55 Carboniferous Volcanics	—	√	√	√	√	—	—	—	—	—	—	√

Notes: (1) In south-west England, the Ten Mile Map uses the numbers 76 to 78 because there is a complete Devonian succession comprising marine and Old Red Sandstone *facies*[A]. (2) As revealed by Lower Lemington borehole. (3) In south-west England, Upper Carboniferous is lumped together as 81–3. (4) Shown only as d[4] on Cheddar 1:25000 cross-section.

ern limb of the syncline are a reflection of the northward directed Variscan movements.

(c) Forest of Dean and Bristol areas: here, two north–south trending synclines preserving Upper Westphalian (83) may be discerned. The Forest of Dean is a basin, but the Bristol coalfield syncline is plunging to the south, with its southern flank largely obscured by Younger Cover.

(d) To the south-west of the Bristol coalfield and in the Mendips in echelon east–west trending folds are present, with steeper northern limbs and some overthrusting.

(e) In south-west England, a very broad syncline is present, with Devonian outcrops in north Devon and Cornwall separated by a central belt of Carboniferous. The outcrop 'stripes' indicate a general east–west trend to the axis of the syncline. Again this a complex syncline because at outcrop intense smaller scale folding can be seen. Although we did not expect you to spot it, it is possible to discern some of this smaller folding on the Ten Mile Map. For example, south of Barnstaple in squares SS(21) 52, 62, 82 and 92, 'fingers' of blue 80 project into 81–3, reflecting the presence of isoclinal folds. Likewise, repetition of 80 inland from Boscastle in squares SX(20) 19 and 28 is also due to the presence of smaller scale folds.

ITQ 28   Sedimentation over the Blocks began later at some localities, whereas in other areas complete successions of Lower Carboniferous are present. For example, on Figure 25, Section 7.2.2, Carboniferous sedimentation begins over the Askrigg Block with 'time slice' 4, and with 5 over the Alston Block, but the adjacent basins contain all the 'time slices' from 1 onwards.

ITQ 29   (a) From Market Weighton northwards as far as the A166 road, the Chalk (106) rests on Lower Lias (91), but to the south on the shores of the Humber, it rests on the Kimmeridge Clay (98–9). Between, the boundary of the Chalk cuts across the boundaries of formations 92 to 97. Therefore, the Chalk must rest *unconformably* on the Jurassic.

(b) At Swanage, there is a *complete* succession of formations (100–105) beneath the Chalk. At Seaton, 70 km to the west, the Upper Greensand (105) rests on topmost Trias (90), and 40 km further west, north of Newton Abbot, it rests on basal Permian (85), Upper Carboniferous (81–3) and Upper Devonian (78). So the Upper Greensand rests *unconformably* on older strata, with the time gap represented by the unconformity increasing in magnitude to the west.

ITQ 30   (a) Permo-Triassic rocks (the New Red Sandstone of the Ten Mile Map) floor most of the Irish Sea depicted on the Lake District map.

(b) Geological cross-section number 2 shows that in addition to the unconformable relationship between the Permo-Triassic and older rocks, the contact shown on the map may sometimes also be a faulted one, with *downthrow*^{A} towards the Irish Sea.

ITQ 31   Along the Cardigan Bay coastline, as shown on the Ten Mile Map, Lower Palaeozoic rocks do not always occur along the coastline. At Harlech and Tywyn, Oligocene (110) occurs. Although it is not possible to tell from the evidence on the map, the contact between the Oligocene and Lower Palaeozoic rocks is faulted, once again downthrown on the seaward side (as on the Lake District map).

ITQ 32   The Vale of Eden, to the south-east of Carlisle, is a good example of a basin in Younger Cover rocks, one side of which is

fault bounded (see map, and the east end of Section 2, particularly the portion showing $2\frac{1}{2}$ times vertical exaggeration). On its western side, Permian strata rest unconformably on Carboniferous strata, but on the eastern margin, Triassic rocks are faulted against Carboniferous *and* Lower Palaeozoic strata. Thus the structure of the Vale of Eden basin is similar to that of Cardigan Bay shown in Figure 35, namely a tilted fault block forming what is often termed a half-graben. The faulted margin of the Vale of Eden Basin is coincident with a fault line that was active during the Early Carboniferous, and defines the western margin of the Alston Block.

ITQ 33   South-western North Sea: I, mixed aeolian and wadi; II, mainly wadi; III, mainly aeolian and interdune sabkhas; IV, marine reworking; V, marine evaporite. South-central North Sea: A, volcanic; B, wadi; C, mixed aeolian and wadi; D, wadi; E, mixed aeolian and wadi; F, inland sabkha; G, desert lake; H, marine evaporite. The top of both successions records the invasion of an inland sea from which, during the Upper Permian, thick evaporites were deposited in the North Sea area.

ITQ 34   In south-east England, Tertiary sediments occur in the Hampshire and London Basins. In north-west Scotland and Northern Ireland, basalt lavas occur, associated with (but dates are not indicated on the Ten Mile Map) dyke swarms and plutonic igneous rocks (granites and gabbros). You may also have noted the relatively small Oligocene outcrops (110) on the coast of Cardigan Bay south of Harlech (SH(23)5830) and in Northern Ireland to the south of Lough Neagh. These deposits are not discussed in this Block.

ITQ 35   The following events appear to be related:

165 Ma	North Africa and North America separated	Middle Jurassic volcanism and uplift in the North Sea
120 Ma	Bay of Biscay opened (Iberia rotated)	Mid-Cretaceous earth movements
80 Ma	North America and Europe separated	Change from a rift to a sag subsidence pattern in the North Sea
52 Ma	Greenland and Europe separated	Tertiary igneous activity during rifting prior to ocean opening
10 Ma	Africa collided with Europe (most recent episode in Alpine orogeny)	Folding and faulting in southern England, probably induced by reactivation of pre-Younger Cover basement faults

Thus, whereas the British Isles occupied a 'mid-plate' position throughout the development of the Younger Cover, it was not immune from the influence of plate tectonic processes operating at the plate margins.

ITQ 36   Drift deposits consist of all non-marine deposits formed during the Quaternary period. In Britain, the chief categories are as follows (you should have listed examples of the first three, as they occur on some of your maps):

Glacial deposits: till (boulder clay), glacial sands and gravels

Fluvial deposits: river gravel and flood plain sands and silts

Slope deposits: head gravel, as on Moreton-in-Marsh sheet, and head, as on Cheddar sheet

Aeolian deposits: dune sands

Lake deposits

SAQ answers and comments

SAQ 1   The table below illustrates the kind of notes you should have made in answering SAQ 1.

	Stratigraphic age of rocks	Igneous activity		Metamorphic rocks present	Structure	
		Intrusive	Extrusive		Major faults	Fold trends, asymmetry
Younger Cover	Permian to Pliocene	Tertiary granites and basic intrusions in W. Islands of Scotland, N. Ireland dyke swarms	Tertiary plateau lavas in W. Scotland, Ireland	None	Fault bounded basins; Mid-Cretaceous faulting	E–W folds folds in S. England, north limbs steeper
		Mesozoic igneous activity in North Sea				
Older Cover	Devonian and Carboniferous	Dykes and sills in Midland Valley	Volcanics in Midland Valley, N. England	None	Midland Valley boundary faults	A variety of trends, N–S in Pennines and Malverns
Variscan orogeny	Devonian and Carboniferous	S.W. England; Permian granites	Lavas	Regional type—produced slates	Southward dipping thrusts on north margin	E–W trending folds, becoming more intense to south
Caledonian orogeny	Late Precambrian to Silurian in Scotland and N. England; Cambrian–Silurian in Wales	Devonian collision granites	Mainly Silurian and Ordovician lavas and pyroclastics	High grade regional in Scotland north of Highland Boundary Fault, largely slates to south	N.W. Scotland; Moine Thrust movement to west; Boundary faults to Midland Valley; Accretionary prism in S. Uplands	Generally trending NE–SW
Precambrian Basement:						
NW Scotland	2 600 Ma to Early Ordovician	Dykes in Lewisian		Lewisian high grade		
elsewhere	Late Precambrian	Late Precambrian granites	Late Precambrian volcanics	Not discussed		

SAQ 2   (a) Evidence for the former existence of the Iapetus Ocean:

(i) palaeomagnetic evidence (see Figure 1)

(ii) the contrasts in the distributions of fossil faunas on either side of Iapetus.

The evidence summarized under (b) and (c) below also supports the former existence of Iapetus, for subduction implies the presence of a downgoing slab of *oceanic* crust.

(b) Evidence for subduction:

(i) accretionary prism in Southern Uplands

(ii) andesitic volcanism in Southern Uplands, the Lake District and Wales.

(c) Evidence for continental collision:

Devonian granites on either side of the Iapetus suture.

You might also have mentioned that reconstructions of Devonian geography suggest a continuous land mass across the British area.

SAQ 3   (a) Figure 50 is a simplified summary log of Carboniferous cyclothems. (b) The relatively short-term changes of relative sea-level implied by the succession may be explained by:

eustatic changes brought about by melting and formation of South Polar ice caps;

epeirogenic changes due to regional uplift and subsidence; delta switching caused by rapid changes in the location of rivers, perhaps due to major floods.

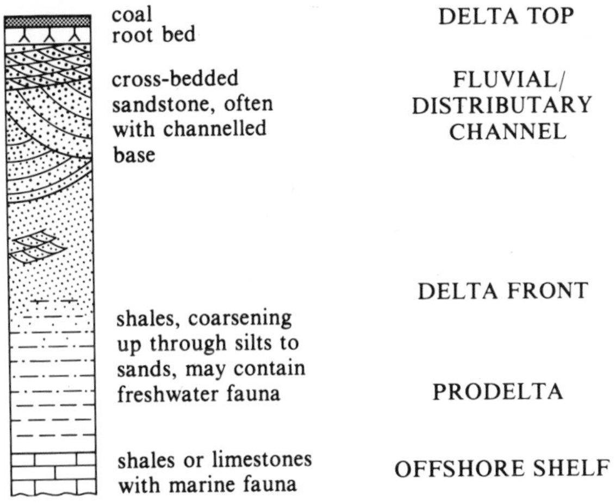

Figure 50 Answer to SAQ 3. Idealized Carboniferous cyclothem: environmental interpretation.

SAQ 4 Examples of the tectonic control of sedimentation patterns described in this Block are:

(i) Accretionary prism of Ordovician and Silurian age in the Southern Uplands (see Figures 9b and 18, Sections 4.4 and 6.2.2).

(ii) Rift-to-sag patterns of sedimentation in the Dalradian of Scotland (Figure 16, Section 6.2.1) and the Carboniferous of the south Pennines (Figure 26, Section 7.2.3).

(iii) Block and basin sedimentation in the Carboniferous (Figure 26).

(iv) Basin and swell sedimentation in the Mesozoic (Figure 37, Section 8.4.2).

If you were particularly sharp you might have mentioned the New Red Sandstone fault-bounded basins, and Mesozoic sedimentation associated with active faults (Figure 36 AA′, Section 8.4.2).

SAQ 5 The following relationships were discussed in this Block:

Eustatic sea-level changes largely appear to be controlled by:

(a) Changes in the volume of ocean ridge systems. During periods of continental separation (see, for example, Figure 3e, Section 2), growth of ridge volume displaces water onto the continents (e.g. during Jurassic and Cretaceous). When continents fuse together, ridge volumes are less, so sea-level falls (e.g. during Carboniferous and Permian).

(b) Changes in the volume of large ice caps. During glacial periods, water is locked into ice caps, causing a sea-level fall (e.g. during Permo-Carboniferous and Quaternary).

Climatic changes may be brought about by:

(a) Continents drifting across latitudes (e.g. changes in Britain from equatorial conditions of the Carboniferous, through the arid zone during the Permo–Trias, to the present-day temperate latitude).

(b) Changes in the configuration of oceans and continents. Thus, towards the end of the Tertiary, the geographic isolation of Antarctica permitted the development of circum-polar ocean currents and winds, which isolated the continent from warmer influences, causing the growth of an ice cap. Likewise, the isolation of the Arctic from other oceans has caused it to be permanently ice covered.

Acknowledgements

The division of this text into Sections dealing with the Orogenic Belts and the Older and Younger Cover is based on a map published in the Geological Museum's booklet *Britain before Man*; the Course Team wish to acknowledge the inspiration this provided in preparing this Block. Constructive comments made by Gareth George and Robert Shackleton on drafts of the text are also gratefully acknowledged.

Grateful acknowledgement is made to the following sources for material used in this block.

Figure 1 from G. C. Brown and A. E. Mussett, *The Inaccessible Earth*, 1981, George Allen & Unwin, redrawn from McElhinny, 1973, by permission of Cambridge University Press; Figure 2(b) from R. Riding, 'Model of the Hercynian Fold Belt' in *Earth and Planetary Science Letters*, vol. 24 (1974), Elsevier Scientific Publishing Co.; Figure 3 from P. J. Wylie, *The Way the Earth Works*, John Wiley & Sons Inc., originally in R. S. Dietz and J. C. Holden, 1970, *Jour. Geophys. Res.*, 75; Figure 4 from C. E. Payton, *Seismic Stratigraphy – Applications to Hydrocarbon Exploration*, 1977, the American Association of Petroleum Geologists; Figure 6 from F. W. Dunning et al., *Britain Before Man*, HMSO for the Institute of Geological Sciences (1978), reproduced by permission of the Controller of HMSO; Figure 8 from G. Boillot, *Geology of the Continental Margins* (trans. A. Scarth), Longman, by permission of Masson S.A., Paris; Figures 13 and 14 from A. L. Harris et al., *The Caledonides of the British Isles – Reviewed*, Scottish Academic Press for the Geological Society of London (1979); Figures 15 and 16 from R. Anderton, Figure 26 from M. R. Leeder, Figure 31 from L. R. Cocks et al., and Figure 32 from R. N. Shackleton et al. and Figure 48 from J. F. Dewey in *Journal of the Geological Society*, vol. 139, Part 4, July 1982, Blackwell Scientific Publications for the Geological Society; Figures 17 and 18 reprinted by permission from *Nature*, vol. 267, 1977, W. S. McKerrow et al. pp. 237–239, copyright © 1977 Macmillan Journals Limited; Figures 23, 24, 25, 30 and 39 from R. Anderton et al., *A Dynamic Stratigraphy of the British Isles*, George Allen & Unwin, 1979; and